READING POWER
TEST BOOKLET

BEATRICE S. MIKULECKY / LINDA JEFFRIES

Longman

Reading Power Test Booklet

Pearson Education, 10 Bank Street, White Plains, NY 10606

Vice president, director of publishing: Allen Ascher
Editorial director: Louisa Hellegers
Acquisitions editor: Laura Le Dréan
Senior development manager: Penny Laporte
Vice president, director of design and production: Rhea Banker
Development editor: Paula H. Van Ells
Production manager: Alana Zdinak
Production supervisor: Liza Pleva
Executive managing editor: Linda Moser
Production editor: Melissa Leyva
Director of manufacturing: Patrice Fraccio
Senior manufacturing buyer: Dave Dickey
Interior design adaptation: DePinho Graphic Design
Composition: ElectraGraphics, Inc.

Text credits: Page 56: From *The Lady in the Lake* by Raymond Chandler, retold by Jennifer Bassett.
    Text copyright © 1991 by Jennifer Bassett. Reproduced courtesy of Penguin Longman
    Publishing. Page 57: From *The Mysterious Island* by Jules Verne, retold by D. K. Swan. Text
    copyright © 1988 by Longman Group UK. Reproduced by permission of the publisher.

ISBN 0-13-027250-7

6 7 8 9 10 -OPM- 08 07

Contents

Introduction

Reading Power Student Book is divided into four parts: Part One: *Reading for Pleasure,* Part Two: *Reading Comprehension Skills,* Part Three: *Thinking Skills,* and Part Four: *Reading Faster.* This booklet includes tests for Part Two and Part Three. No formal tests for Part One and Part Four are included because the skills developed in these parts are not amenable to group testing. However, the booklet does offer a variety of ideas and activities for evaluating these aspects of reading development on an individual basis.

Some of the later exercises in each unit of the Student Book can also be used to evaluate student progress. Teachers who decide to use those exercises for that purpose should have students remove the Answer Key from the back of their books (pages 275–287) at the beginning of the semester. These pages have been perforated for easy removal. The Answer Key can be stapled and collected. Teachers can then redistribute answers to the tests on occasions when students need to check them on their own.

If you would like to read more about the teaching of reading, we suggest the following texts:

Brown, D. *A World of Books: An Annotated Reading List for ESL/EFL Students,* TESOL, 1988.

Brown, D. *Books for a Small Planet: A Multicultural-Intercultural Bibliography for Young English Language Learners,* TESOL, 1994.

Carter, R., and M. McCarthy. *Vocabulary and Language Teaching,* Longman, 1988.

Day, R. (ed.). *New Ways in Teaching Reading,* TESOL, 1993.

Day, R., and J. Bamford. *Extensive Reading in the Second Language Classroom,* Cambridge University Press, 1998.

Mikulecky, B. *A Short Course in Teaching Reading Skills,* Addison Wesley Longman, 1990.

Part One

Evaluating Reading for Pleasure

Before starting work in Reading for Pleasure, teachers are strongly urged to read the teacher's notes for Part One on pages 290–293 in the Teacher's Guide at the end of the Student Book. In these pages, teachers will find both practical suggestions for organizing reading for pleasure in class and an explanation of the rationale and objectives of this part of the book. Also included are ideas for evaluating students' progress in their pleasure-reading books, which are expanded on here.

There are a number of reasons to evaluate students' progress in Reading for Pleasure. First, teachers may need to verify that students have read what they say they have read. Teachers may also be required by the school to provide an assessment of the students' work. From the students' point of view, the fact that teachers spend classroom time on evaluation or follow-up activities encourages students to take their reading for pleasure more seriously. Furthermore, activities that involve sharing the reading experience with other students can provide additional opportunities for practice in speaking and writing.

Teachers should be careful, however, not to overdo the follow-up activities and so take all the pleasure out of pleasure reading. Students who are often required to follow up their reading with tedious exercises may come to dread finishing a book. Many exercises often seem like "busywork" to students, without relevance to them and their reading experience. In fact, outside the classroom when people talk or write about books, they usually focus only on their reaction to the book; they examine their own personal response and share their response with others. The same should be true in the classroom. The activities proposed here try to adhere to this principle.

One further note of caution: ***Teachers need to keep in mind that the real purpose of reading for pleasure (also known as extensive reading) is to encourage students to read as much as possible.*** However valid a follow-up activity, it cannot replace the reading itself. Teachers must take care not to permit follow-up evaluation activities to take up classroom or homework time that could be spent reading.

1 Oral activities for evaluation

Book conferences

As mentioned in the Teacher's Guide, these brief conversations with individual students about their books can provide valuable feedback on students' reading. With the teacher's questions as a model for the kind of language to use, students also develop their ability to engage in discussions about books and ideas.

Book discussion groups

As an alternative or in addition to the individual conferences, teachers can organize regular book discussions in pairs or small groups—not more than four students. The following are some general guidelines for book discussion groups:

1. Groups can be formed randomly or according to shared reading interests (e.g., a group of students who love thrillers).
2. In each discussion session, students report in turn on their progress in reading their book.
3. The reports should be brief—not more than three minutes—and informal, with no written preparation.
4. To prevent students from speaking for too long, one student in each group could be given the job of timing the others.
5. To ensure that all members are listening, each group member could be required to ask a question after a student has finished talking.
6. Students should be told not to summarize the plot, and especially not to reveal the ending, but rather to speak about their reactions to the book. These discussions can lead to students exchanging books when they have finished reading them.

While these discussions are going on, the teacher can circulate and listen in or comment on the students' views or reactions. The teacher may not be able to hear every student during one discussion session, but if the groups meet frequently, teachers will be able to get a good idea of how the students are progressing.

Book talks

As mentioned in the Teacher's Guide, a good way for the teacher to inform students about books is to give "book talks" to the class. These should be short and personal and should convey enthusiasm for the book. In these talks, teachers give a brief introduction to a book's content and a general reaction to various aspects of the book such as character, mood, and the author's intentions. After a few of these talks, the teacher can then ask students to give similar talks, either in front of the whole class or in smaller groups.

Students who are less confident about their oral skills may work better with a skeleton outline to help them. For example:

Introduction:	Title and author
	Type of book. (e.g., mystery)
	Length and difficulty
Body:	What I liked about the book and why (characters, mood, setting, style, subject matter, a favorite passage)
	What I did not like about the book, if anything
Conclusion:	I recommend/don't recommend this book

2 *Written activities for evaluation*

Record of books read

One useful tool for measuring students' progress in reading books for pleasure is a simple list of the books students read. They can write down basic information about the books in their notebooks or on a separate hand-out constructed by the teacher. A frequent look at this list will allow teachers to get some idea of what their students are reading. Any doubts about whether a student has really read all the books on his/her list may be dispelled with a few quick questions about the books.

The idea of keeping a record of books read can be expanded to include a sentence or two with the reader's opinion of each book. These opinions can be shared with the rest of the class to give others ideas about which books they might enjoy. There are several ways to organize this sharing of opinions. One way is to ask students to fill out a note card with basic information and a brief opinion after they finish a book (as in the Pleasure Reading Report on page 14 of the Student Book). These note cards can then be kept on file in the classroom to be consulted by students looking for reading suggestions. Alternatively, the book reports can be kept in a binder, with a page for each book on which students note their opinions.

Book reviews

Teachers should avoid the classic book report that simply summarizes a book. These reports are uninteresting to write and to read.

One way to ask students to write about a book is to have them write a letter to a friend. A form for this is found on page 13 of the Student Book. An alternative would be to have students write an e-mail message, which they could actually send if computers and e-mail are available to students.

Teachers can also assign a different kind of report in which students write about one or two aspects of their personal reaction to a book. Students can be given a list of possibilities from which to choose one or two to write about. The following list is adapted from Day and Bamford (p. 143):

- Characters that students identify with
- Points of the story or behavior that interest students
- Personal experiences or thoughts related to the book
- Favorite parts of the book
- Parts of the book or characters that students dislike
- Larger issues dealt with or raised by the book (e.g., war, sexism)

Students at this level cannot be expected to write more than a few sentences or a paragraph about their books. It is important for this activity that their writing not be judged for its grammatical or syntactical correctness. The teacher should respond only to what the student is saying about the book. This can be done either by commenting on the student's reaction or, if the teacher has read the book, by giving his or her own reaction. Aside from being more stimulating to write and read, these reaction reports have another advantage over the traditional book report: It is difficult, if not impossible, for a student to invent a reaction without having read the book.

The concept of writing opinions about books can be extended to include book reviews for a classroom newsletter or a newsletter put together for the whole English-language program.

Student-generated comprehension questions

In the traditional reading classroom, students are often asked to respond to comprehension questions at the end of a reading. For students, this task often becomes mechanical and again has little relation to their reading experience. These exercises can be made more relevant by asking questions about the reader's understanding of the author's intentions or about the reader's reaction to some aspect of the text.

For working on pleasure reading, however, there is another problem with teacher-generated comprehension questions. Since the students are all reading different books, which the teacher may or may not have read, it is not easy to come up with questions for each book. The solution to this problem could be to ask students to write their own questions. Before doing this, they need some guidance about what kinds of questions are appropriate and how to write them.

If students have had at least one book conference with the teacher, they will be familiar with the types of question that are appropriate. The best questions for pleasure reading are not literal questions that test for memory of the book. The best questions are elaborative, that is, questions that allow students to elaborate on the book and deepen their own awareness of it. The following list is taken from Mikulecky, *A Short Course in Teaching Reading Skills*, pages 19–20.

Elaborative Question Types

Expressive	How did you like the book?
Factual	Who is the main character? Where is the story set?
Informational	What was it about?
Experiential	Did anything like that ever happen to you?
Affective	How did that make you feel?
Relational	Did you ever hear of anything like this in your country (or neighborhood)?
Critical	Do you think that this could really happen?
Predictive	What do you think will happen next?
Stylistic	Did the author do a good job in making that character seem real?
Sequential	What happened after that?
Cause/Effect	What made the tree fall into the road?
Summarizing	Can you tell the whole story in just a few sentences?
Speculative	What would this story be like if someone else were telling the story?
Inferential	Why do you think the character behaved as he or she did in that situation?

Predictions about books

Predictions can be used for several purposes. First, asking students who are part way through a book to predict how they think it will end stimulates them to reflect on what they are reading and to use their imagination. It also is another way for teachers to show interest in students' reading and to measure students' progress. Students can write down their prediction for the teacher to collect and then hand back when the book has been finished. Students can then compare what they predicted with the actual ending.

Following this activity, students could write about their reactions to the actual ending of their book and whether they liked it. They can then be asked to imagine and write about an alternative ending or even a sequel, if they think the book could be continued.

3   *Negotiated evaluations*

One further possibility teachers may want to consider, depending on their teaching contexts, is to allow students to decide together how they would prefer to have their reading evaluated. Dupuy, Tse, and Cook suggest that this approach "can be quite liberating for both the teacher and the student. Also, in this way, the process of creating independent readers—from choosing their own books to evaluating their own reading progress—is complete" (p. 14).

Furthermore, "students choosing their own evaluation are more likely to select projects that are interesting and meaningful to them, and in turn, give a more accurate demonstration of their ability and proficiency than standardized or imposed evaluations" (p. 14). Contrary to what some teachers might expect, students do not generally choose easy assignments for themselves; they tend to take this responsibility quite seriously. Teachers might need to start by presenting some oral or written options. Dupuy, Tse, and Cook list the following examples of student-generated evaluation projects: "creating mock news broadcasts or news reports of selected events in the stories, writing a 'diary' of one or more characters, forming book promotion teams to introduce books to other classes, writing sequels to stories or books, creating comic books or simplified versions of a book for less proficient students to read" (p. 14).

Further reading

Day, R., and J. Bamford. *Extensive Reading in the Second Language Classroom*, Cambridge University Press, New York, 1998.

Dupuy, B., L. Tse, and T. Cook. "Bringing Books into the Classroom: First Steps in Turning College-Level ESL Students into Readers," *TESOL Journal*, Summer 1996.

Mikulecky, B. S. *A Short Course in Teaching Reading Skills*, Addison Wesley Longman, White Plains, NY, 1990

Part Two

Evaluating Reading Comprehension Skills

―――――

In *Reading Power,* reading comprehension is viewed as a thinking process and reading comprehension skills are seen as they fit into the process. This approach is explained in detail on pages 293–297 of the Teacher's Guide in the Student Book and in *A Short Course in Teaching Reading Skills,* by Beatrice S. Mikulecky. The reading comprehension skills units in the Student Book are designed to make students consciously aware of the thinking process that good readers of English employ while they are reading. It is this awareness, together with practice in the specific skills, that makes it possible for students to improve their comprehension.

Research has shown that a test best measures the level of mastery of a skill or trait when the test reflects the format of the training. Therefore, the tests on comprehension skills in this booklet are similar in format to the exercises in each unit. In all of these activities, a primary aim is to lead students to explore their thinking processes and to open a window through which teacher and student can examine those processes. The aim of the teacher in testing students should be to verify how well students have understood and mastered the thinking processes involved in using each of the skills presented.

Teachers also need to approach the students' responses to these tests as they would to responses to exercises in the Student Book. That is, since no two students think exactly alike, they may often respond differently and their responses may not coincide exactly with the answer given in the Answer Key. The Answer Key should be taken as an indication of a possible answer, but any responses that students can reasonably justify should be accepted.

Undoubtedly, scoring tests that include open-ended questions or asking students to explain their answers will require more time and effort on the part of the teacher. However, this will allow the teacher to get a more accurate sense of each student's progress than would otherwise be possible. It should also be noted that the responsibility and extra time involved are not so different from what is required of a teacher of composition who aims to lead students to a better understanding of the thinking process required to express themselves clearly in English.

Unit 1: **Scanning**

Test 1

➤ *You are planning to take a cruise vacation. Scan "Free Cruise Information" on page 8 to find the answers to these questions. You do not need to write complete sentences. Time limit: 4 minutes.*

1. How many free brochures can you get? _____

2. Which cruises go to Africa? _____

3. Which cruise goes by steamboat on American rivers? _____

4. Which two cruises travel to Alaska? _____

5. Which cruise line explores Europe's famous rivers and cities? _____

6. What is the telephone number of the cruise line that goes to Greece? _____

7. What special cruises does South Pacific Cruise Lines offer? _____

8. How many ships does the Olympia Cruise Company have? _____

9. What is the address of Ocean Cruise Travel? _____

10. When does the coupon expire? _____

FREE CRUISE INFORMATION

GUIDE to VACATIONS
on the BEST SHIPS and SAILING BOATS

Send for free information about the cruise ship lines listed below.

1. **Famous Cruises.** Beyond your wildest dreams on celebrity-packed cruises to Alaska, Bermuda, South America, and Europe. Call 1-800-FAMOUS1 for a free brochure.
2. **Precious Cruises.** Europe's #1 passenger ship line offers the cruise of your dreams throughout the Mediterranean and Southern Europe. Send for a free brochure.
3. **Worldwide Line.** Sail across the Atlantic Ocean or around the world. Enjoy exquisite pampering, the highest level of service, fascinating companions, special destinations, and cultural outings. Call your travel advisor or 1-800-OURWORLD.
4. **Delta Princess Steamship.** Enjoy America's most beautiful rivers by steamboat. Cruises from 4–10 nights. Free brochure. Call 1-800-DELTAONE.
5. **Amsterdam Lines.** Explore Europe's famous rivers and cities on our floating hotel. Call our office soon. 1-800-YOURLINE
6. **South Pacific Cruise Lines.** Our tours visit Australia, New Zealand, Africa, and India, with special cruises to the South Pacific and Antarctica. Free brochure available.
7. **Royal Queen Cruises.** The most famous cruises to Alaska. Cruise the Inside Passage all the way up to Alaska and the North Pole. Free Alaska planning kit and video! Free brochure.
8. **Olympia Cruises.** Only on our three specialized cruise ships can you choose your level of luxury as you cruise the isles of Greece, the coasts of Italy, and intriguing ports in North Africa. Call 1-800-OLYMPICO.

clip and mail now!

SALE INFORMATION

To request sale information and discount offers on any of the advertisers listed above, circle the corresponding number(s), fill in the mailing information, and mail to the address below.

1	2	3	4
5	6	7	8

PLEASE SEND COUPON TO:

OCEAN CRUISE TRAVEL
P.O. Box 1234
Rosebud, NJ 98765-4321

Please fill in this information:

NAME _____

ADDRESS _____

CITY _____

STATE _____

ZIP _____

PHONE _____

(This coupon expires on April 1, 2003)

Unit 2: **Previewing and Predicting**

Test 1

➤ *Predict what will come next in each group of sentences. Choose the letter of the sentence that could come next.*

1. It was a hot, sunny day in Miami. The beach was crowded with happy tourists.
   a. No one was swimming because the water was so cold.
   b. Many people were wearing raincoats and carrying umbrellas.
   c. Swimmers enjoyed the warm ocean water.

2. There was nothing good to watch on TV last night. The Ruiz family did not want to go out.
   a. They decided to go visit their friends.
   b. They decided to play a game of cards.
   c. They went shopping.

3. Simon finished college in May and he moved to Queens, New York, in July. He found a new job and a nice apartment to share with two friends.
   a. In September he will go back to college.
   b. His friends have also found new jobs in New York.
   c. He likes living alone.

4. Bianca is a medical student in Chicago. She comes from a small town in the country, so she is not used to big cities.
   a. Her sister lives in New York and her brother lives in Los Angeles.
   b. She has lived in Chicago all of her life and she hopes to leave soon.
   c. Many things about Chicago were surprising to her at first.

5. Sam loves Italian music, and yesterday he attended a concert given by a famous Italian singer.
   a. He had never heard Italian music before.
   b. The concert was held in Symphony Hall.
   c. Sam could not get a ticket for the concert.

6. Lee is planning another trip to Hawaii. She loves the beaches and palm trees on the islands.
   a. She wants to do a lot of ice-skating while she is there.
   b. Lee has never been to Hawaii before, so she plans to take many pictures.
   c. She also likes to eat the delicious pineapples and other Hawaiian fruit.

7. Travel by train is very pleasant. The seats are comfortable and you can walk around if you get tired of sitting.
   a. Many trains have dining cars for meals.
   b. Tickets for train travel are expensive and hard to find.
   c. When you get off the train, it is easy to get lost in the station.

8. Travel by plane is sometimes unpleasant these days. You may have to wait a long time to take off. The seats in many planes are small and uncomfortable.
   a. The movie is often boring.
   b. The food is usually very good.
   c. You can meet interesting people on the plane.

Unit 2:   **Previewing and Predicting**

Test 2

➤ *Preview this passage. Remember, you should read only some parts of it. Do not try to read the whole passage! Time limit: 30 seconds. Then answer the questions on the next page.*

Grandmother Saved After Accident

On Monday evening, Mrs. Millie Moore was driving to the airport in Fort Lauderdale, Florida. She was going to the airport to meet Lisa, her granddaughter. Lisa came to visit her every summer for a few weeks. Mrs. Moore was very happy about the visit. Now, in the car, she was not so happy about driving to the airport. She was eighty-three years old and she did not like driving in the dark. But the airport was only twenty minutes from her house, so she tried not to worry.

Halfway to the airport, there was a bridge. As she was driving over it, a large truck came up suddenly from behind and hit her car. Before she knew it, Mrs. Moore's car was flying off the bridge, upside down. It landed in the middle of lots of trees and hung there, still upside down. Mrs. Moore was lucky. She was wearing her seatbelt, so she was not seriously hurt. But she could not get out of the car. The truck driver drove away.

When Mrs. Moore did not meet Lisa at the airport, her family was worried. They called the police and the police began to look for her. They drove right over the bridge several times but did not see her car. No one could see it because it was covered by trees. After two days, the police stopped looking.

Then on Thursday morning, some road workers were picking up trash on the bridge. One of the workers looked down through the trees. At first, he saw just a piece of metal. Then he could see the whole car. He looked more closely and he saw a person's leg! He called the police and an ambulance. Then, with the other workers, he climbed down to the car.

They found Mrs. Moore, who said, "Can you please get me out of here?"

It was not easy to get her out. They had to call the firemen for some special ladders. When Mrs. Moore finally arrived at the hospital, her family was waiting. She told them about her three days in the car. There was no food in the car, but she was lucky. She had a plastic bag with her and she could catch some rain water in the bag, so she had something to drink.

Mrs. Moore spent two days in the hospital, resting. She was very glad to go home and enjoy the company of her whole family.

Do not look back at the passage. There is no time limit on this part. Answer the questions.

1. Why was Mrs. Moore going to the airport?
   a. Because she liked driving.
   b. To meet her granddaughter.
   c. Because it was only twenty minutes away.

2. What happened to Mrs. Moore's car?
   a. It hit a truck.
   b. It did not start.
   c. It went off a bridge.

3. Why did no one find Mrs. Moore for three days?
   a. Because her car was under water.
   b. Because no one looked for her.
   c. Because the car was covered by trees.

4. Who found Mrs. Moore?
   a. Some road workers.
   b. The police.
   c. Her family.

What can you predict? What will happen next to the people in the story? Write your answer below.

_____

_____

_____

Unit 3: **Building a Powerful Vocabulary**

❖ *Using the context to guess words*

Test 1

➤ *Read the whole passage. Then go back and write one word in each blank space. All the missing words are at the end of the passage.*

Amelia Earhart

Amelia Earhart was born in 1897 in Atchison, Kansas. There was an airport

near her _____. Amelia loved watching the planes at the airport. She decided
          (1)

that she _____ to learn to fly some day.
          (2)

After college, Amelia got her _____ license. Then she flew her own plane
                              (3)

in air shows in California _____ a few years.
                          (4)

In those days, pilots were trying to _____ longer and longer flights. In
                                     (5)

1928, two men were planning _____ fly across the Atlantic Ocean. They
                            (6)

invited Amelia to go with _____. During the flight, she wrote notes about it.
                         (7)

Then she wrote a book called *20 Hrs. 40 Min.*

In 1932, Amelia was _____ first woman to fly across the Atlantic Ocean
                    (8)

alone. It was a difficult and _____ flight. She flew through a storm and her
                             (9)

plane had some problems. In fact, she _____ not get all the way to England.
                                      (10)

She had to land in a cow field in Ireland. Her _____ made a new record of
                                               (11)

thirteen hours and thirty minutes. Her next big adventure came a few _____
                                                                     (12)

later. In 1935, Amelia flew her plane across the Pacific Ocean. She was the

_____ woman to do that, too.
(13)

After that, Amelia wanted to _____ for another record. She wanted to be
                             (14)

the first person to fly _____ the world at the equator. She asked her friend
                       (15)

Fred Noonan to go with _____. They left the United States on June 1, 1937,
                       (16)

going east. A _____ (17) later, they were most of the way around the world. On

July 2, people were _____ (18) for them at Howland Island, in the Pacific Ocean.

Amelia and Fred _____ (19) arrived.

People looked for the plane for weeks but they did not _____ (20) it. Now they

believe it fell into the ocean. However, no one really knows what happened.

around	dangerous	did	find	first	flight	for
her	home	make	month	never	pilot's	the
them	to	try	waiting	wanted	years	

Unit 3: **Building a Powerful Vocabulary**

❖ *Using the context to guess words*

Test 2

➤ *Read the whole passage. Then go back and write one word in each blank space. All the missing words are at the end of the passage.*

Abraham Lincoln's Early Years

Abraham Lincoln was the sixteenth president of the United States and served from 1861–1865. He was born in Kentucky in 1809. When he was _____ (1) years old, his family moved to Indiana. They lived in a _____ (2) house in the forest, and they were very poor. Abraham had _____ (3) work hard to help his family. He was able to go to _____ (4) for only a year. However, his family gave him books and he learned to _____ (5) and write well.

When Abraham was nineteen years old, his family _____ (6) again, to Illinois. He helped his father build a new house. _____ (7) he went to work for his neighbors. Later, he got a _____ (8) building boats. As part of the job, he took a trip _____ (9) the Mississippi River to New Orleans. This was an important experience for _____ (10). In New Orleans, he saw black African slaves for the first _____ (11). In fact, he saw white men buying and selling slaves. He _____ (12) then that slavery was a terrible thing and he wanted to _____ (13) something to stop it.

Soon after that, Abraham started working at a store in New Salem, Illinois. The people there liked Abraham. He _____ (14) honest, intelligent, and hard working. People often stopped at the store to _____ (15) to him.

All this time, Abraham continued reading a lot. He read _____ about
(16)

grammar, history, and law. He read poetry, Shakespeare, and the Bible. He read

_____ the magazines and newspapers in his store.
(17)

Then, in 1834, _____ decided to enter politics. That was the beginning
(18)

of his fight to _____ slavery. In fact, slavery ended in the United States in
(19)

1865, _____ he was president.
(20)

Abraham	all	books	decided	do	down	him
job	little	moved	read	school	seven	stop
talk	then	time	to	was	while	

Unit 3: **Building a Powerful Vocabulary**

❖ *Guessing meaning from context*

Test 1

➤ **Guess the general meaning of the word from the context. Write the general meaning of the word on the line.**

1. Joanne loved to help her mother make bread. When they finished, however, Joanne was always covered with flour. There was flour all over the kitchen, too.

   What does "flour" mean? _____

   _____

2. If you put some sugar in a glass of water, it dissolves. It dissolves more quickly in warm water than in cold water.

   What does "dissolves" mean? _____

   _____

3. Please stop bothering me! I'm trying to study. If you keep coming in to ask me things, I can't think. Leave me alone!

   What does "bothering" mean? _____

   _____

4. It was very exciting to be in the wilderness for the first time. There were mountains and forests all around us. And there were no other people for hundreds of miles.

   What does "wilderness" mean? _____

   _____

5. George and Dan set off very early in the morning. They wanted to get to the river before daylight because that was the best time for catching fish.

   What does "set off" mean? _____

   _____

Unit 3: **Building a Powerful Vocabulary**

❖ *Guessing meaning from context*

Test 2

➤ *Guess the general meaning of the word from the context. Write the general meaning of the word on the line.*

1. The little boy was not dressed for the Canadian winter weather. He was wearing shorts and a shirt with short sleeves and he was very cold.

   What does "sleeve" mean? _____

   _____

2. The old house was a creepy place. It was very big and dark, and it made strange noises in the night. I closed my door and got into bed, but I couldn't go to sleep.

   What does "creepy" mean? _____

   _____

3. Dario buys whole coffee beans from Colombia. Every morning he grinds the beans for his breakfast coffee. He says the coffee tastes much better this way.

   What does "grind" mean? _____

   _____

4. This knife is very blunt. I can't even cut a tomato with it! Do you have another knife that cuts better?

   What does "blunt" mean? _____

   _____

5. Be careful! Don't touch that cat. You could get hurt. It's not a friendly cat and sometimes it scratches and bites people.

   What does "scratches" mean? _____

   _____

Unit 3: **Building a Powerful Vocabulary**

❖ *Guessing meaning from context*

Test 3

➤ *Read the passage. The underlined words may be new to you. Use only the context of the passage to guess the meaning of the words you do not know. Then do the test items that follow.*

Whales

Whales are like fish in many ways. Their bodies are similar. Both whales and fish have side <u>fins</u> and tail fins for swimming. However, there is a difference in the tail fins. The tail fins of whales are horizontal (sideways), while the tail fins of fish are vertical (up-and-down). In fact, you can always tell a whale from a fish by its tail fins.

5   There is also another, more important difference. Unlike a fish, the whale is a <u>mammal</u>. It <u>breathes</u> air. Fish stay underwater all the time, but whales have to come up to the <u>surface</u> to get air. They breathe through a hole in the top of their heads. First they blow out the old air mixed with water. Then they breathe in new air. This makes a strange, loud, breathing sound. You can sometimes hear this breathing from

10 far away. You can also see the air and water when the whale breathes out.

Like other mammals, <u>female</u> whales <u>give birth</u> to live babies. The babies are born underwater, but they cannot stay underwater for long. The mother pushes her baby to the surface to breathe. Usually, there are other female whales nearby. They may help the mother push the baby to the surface or they may just touch her and "talk"

15 to her.

Baby whales drink milk from their mothers. They grow very quickly. They may <u>gain</u> as much as 8 or 10 pounds a day. This is possible because they drink a lot of milk (up to 50 liters a day). Baby whales <u>nurse</u> for about a year. Then they start to eat the same food their parents eat.

20 There are two kinds of whales: baleen whales and toothed whales. The baleen whales have no teeth. They include the blue whale, the largest animal on earth. These <u>huge</u> whales eat the smallest animals in the sea, called krill. In one mouthful, they may eat up to 50,000 krill. The toothed whales have a very different <u>diet</u>. They use their teeth to hunt and eat fish or other sea animals.

25 Whales are very <u>sociable</u> animals. The females and young whales live together in groups and the males sometimes <u>join</u> these groups. When they are together, whales communicate with each other. They can make a clicking sound with their heads. Scientists believe that whales have conversations with their clicks. However, no one knows what they are saying to each other.

➤ **A. Check the meanings of the underlined words in the passage. The underlined words are in Column 1. The meanings are in Column 2. Write the letter of the best meaning after each word. You may look back at the passage.**

Column 1

1. fins _____
2. mammal _____
3. breathe _____
4. surface _____
5. female _____
6. give birth _____
7. gain _____
8. nurse _____
9. huge _____
10. diet _____
11. sociable _____
12. join _____

Column 2

a. take in air and let it out again
b. food
c. the sex that has babies
d. become part of
e. very large
f. the place where water meets the air
g. part of the body of fish or whales
h. friendly with each other
i. have a baby
j. increase or become more
k. when a baby drinks its mother's milk
l. animal that breathes air and gives birth to live babies

➤ **B. Circle the letter of the best ending to complete each of the following sentences about the passage. You may look back at the passage.**

1. Whales and fish
   a. are the same.
   b. have different fins.
   c. have the same tails.

2. When a whale breathes,
   a. you can see and hear it.
   b. it is usually underwater.
   c. it looks like a fish.

3. Baby whales
   a. are born near a beach.
   b. stay underwater for a year.
   c. have to go up to breathe.

4. Baleen whales and toothed whales
   a. both eat small sea animals called krill.
   b. have teeth for killing fish.
   c. eat different kinds of food.

5. Whales
   a. often fight each other for food.
   b. like to be with other whales.
   c. usually do not live in groups.

Unit 3: **Building a Powerful Vocabulary**

❖ *Guessing meaning from context*

Test 4

➤ *Read the passage. The underlined words may be new to you. Use only the context of the passage to guess the meaning of the words you do not know. Then do the test items that follow.*

Pablo Picasso

Pablo Picasso was one of the great artists of the twentieth century. Many people believe that he was, in fact, the greatest. He was born in 1881, in Malaga, Spain. His father was an art teacher, and Picasso showed interest in art very early in his life.

He studied art first in Barcelona and then in Madrid. Between 1900 and 1904, he
5   made several visits to Paris. In 1904, he decided to live there. Paris at that time was a very <u>lively</u> place. Many interesting artists, musicians, <u>poets</u>, and <u>novelists</u> were living in the French capital. Some were French, but there were also many people from other European countries and from America.

Picasso soon made friends with the artists in Paris. He became an <u>influential</u>
10   person in the art world and his pictures changed the history of art. His early pictures were mostly <u>realistic</u>. The people and things in the pictures usually looked real. During this <u>phase</u>, Picasso got many of his ideas from the art of <u>ancient</u> Greece and Rome.

In 1907, Picasso painted one of his most famous pictures, "Les Demoiselles
15   d'Avignon." There are four women in this picture, but they do not look very much like women. Their bodies are shown as <u>geometric</u> shapes. In fact, Picasso was not interested any more in painting the real world. He was interested in painting <u>abstract</u> pictures. In these paintings, he did not show people or things as they really were. He showed them as shapes or colors. He was interested in the way these shapes
20   and colors looked next to each other.

Many people did not like this new kind of art. They said it was not art at all. However, other artists understood what Picasso was doing. Many of them followed his ideas and began painting abstract pictures, too. Soon, he was making another new kind of painting. For these, Picasso used paint together with paper and cloth.
25   Again, not everyone liked these pictures, but they became famous, too.

In 1914, Picasso moved to the south of France. He lived there for the rest of his long life. Many more great art works followed his early ones. One of them, titled "Guernica," was painted in 1937. It showed the terrible <u>suffering</u> of the Spanish people during the Spanish Civil War. Near the end of his life, Picasso worked for
30   world peace. His picture of two flying <u>doves</u> is a well-known <u>symbol</u> of peace. Picasso died in 1973 at the age of ninety-three.

➤ **A. Check the meanings of the underlined words in the passage. The underlined words are in Column 1. The meanings are in Column 2. Write the letter of the best meaning after each word. You may look back at the passage.**

Column 1

1. lively _____

2. poets _____

3. novelists _____

4. influential _____

5. realistic _____

6. phase _____

7. ancient _____

8. geometric _____

9. abstract _____

10. suffering _____

11. doves _____

12. symbol _____

Column 2

a. important

b. people who write poetry

c. from a very long time ago (more than 1,000 years)

d. like in real life

e. pain and unhappiness

f. with shapes and colors, not real things

g. a thing that has a special meaning

h. full of interesting people with new ideas

i. period of time

j. people who write novels

k. in the shape of circles, lines, squares, etc.

l. birds

➤ **B. Circle the letter of the best ending to complete each of the following sentences about the passage. You may look back at the passage.**

1. Picasso moved to Paris because
   a. it was full of Spanish people.
   b. it was lively and full of artists.
   c. his father was living there.

2. In Paris, Picasso
   a. was very successful.
   b. did not paint any pictures.
   c. painted pictures of the city.

3. In 1907, Picasso painted
   a. some women he knew.
   b. people from ancient Greece.
   c. abstract pictures.

4. Many artists
   a. painted pictures like Picasso's pictures.
   b. were more famous than Picasso.
   c. painted pictures of people at war.

5. Picasso
   a. painted only people.
   b. was interested in world problems.
   c. never thought about world problems.

Unit 3: **Building a Powerful Vocabulary**

❖ *Using pronouns*

Test 1

➤ *There are 20 pronouns underlined in this passage. After you have read the passage, write the pronouns and referents on the lines provided.*

Passenger Saves Bus and Passengers

When Eldridge Roberts left home yesterday morning, <u>he</u> was late for work. <u>He</u>
(1)   (2)
couldn't drive his car because <u>it</u> needed new brakes. <u>He</u> had to take the bus instead.
(3)   (4)
Carrying his lunch in a brown bag, he hurried to the bus stop and caught Bus 54 to

Paterson, New Jersey. <u>He</u> did not want to be late for his new job.
(5)

5   Mr. Roberts sat down four seats behind the driver. <u>He</u> looked at his watch and <u>he</u>
(6)   (7)
looked at the road. Fortunately, there was not a lot of traffic. A few minutes later, the

bus was going about 35 miles (50 kilometers) per hour down Jersey Avenue.

Suddenly Mr. Roberts saw that something was wrong with the bus driver. <u>He</u> was
(8)
face down on the steering wheel. <u>He</u> was not steering the bus.
(9)

10   Mr. Roberts ran to the front of the bus. <u>It</u> was already out of control. <u>He</u> tried to
(10)   (11)
put his foot on the brakes, but the driver's feet were in the way. So Mr. Roberts sat

next to <u>him</u> and tried to steer the bus. <u>It</u> was going straight toward a big stone wall.
(12)   (13)
The frightened passengers started screaming. <u>They</u> were terrified. Mr. Roberts
(14)
turned the steering wheel toward the right. The bus missed the wall and went off

15   the street. <u>It</u> went onto a big empty field. Then <u>it</u> went through a fence and into
(15)   (16)
someone's backyard. Mr. Roberts saw a house coming closer. <u>He</u> fell to the floor
(17)
of the bus.

Fortunately, the bus stopped six feet from the house. Mr. Roberts and the other

passengers got out of the bus through the emergency door at the back.

Reading Power Test Booklet   *23*

Name _____ Date _____

20   The police and ambulances came to take <u>them</u> to a nearby hospital. The bus driver,
(18)

Jim Fort, age thirty-eight, had died of a heart attack. No one else was seriously hurt.

Mr. Roberts got a ride from one of the policemen. When <u>he</u> finally got to work it was
(19)

almost noon. His new boss treated <u>him</u> to lunch, since his own lunch was still on the bus.
(20)

Pronouns   *Referents*

1. __he__   <u>Eldridge Roberts</u> _____

2. _____   _____

3. _____   _____

4. _____   _____

5. _____   _____

6. _____   _____

7. _____   _____

8. _____   _____

9. _____   _____

10. _____   _____

11. _____   _____

12. _____   _____

13. _____   _____

14. _____   _____

15. _____   _____

16. _____   _____

17. _____   _____

18. _____   _____

19. _____   _____

20. _____   _____

24   **Reading Power Test Booklet**

© 2001 by Addison Wesley Longman, Inc.
A Pearson Education company.
Duplication for classroom use is permitted.

Unit 3: **Building a Powerful Vocabulary**

❖ *Using pronouns*

Test 2

➤ *The pronouns in these sentences are underlined. Circle the referents.*

EXAMPLE

(Washington, D.C.,) is the capital of the United States. <u>It</u> is the only American city that is not in a state.

1. Sometimes people think that Washington, D.C., is the same as Washington State, but <u>they</u> are thousands of miles apart.
2. Washington State is in the northwestern part of the United States. <u>It</u> is on the Pacific Ocean.
3. Olympia, the capital city of Washington State, is not the biggest city in the state. <u>That</u> is Seattle, a city with a population of about 540,000.
4. In the southwestern part of Washington State, there is a volcano named Mount St. Helens. For hundreds of years, <u>it</u> was quiet. Then, in the spring of 1980, the volcano began to erupt.
5. Tourists in Seattle often go to visit the Boeing factory near the city. <u>That</u> is where jumbo jets are made. The building is so large <u>it</u> sometimes has rain clouds up near the roof.
6. People in Seattle love their many parks. One of <u>them</u> is Kobe Park. <u>It</u> is named after Seattle's sister city in Japan.
7. Seattle is a city of immigrants. Many of <u>them</u> come from China, Japan, Korea, Vietnam, and other countries in Asia.
8. In some areas of Washington State, there are very old, large trees. Until recently, people could cut <u>them</u> down for the wood. Now the United States government is trying to stop <u>that</u>.
9. Near Seattle there are many islands. Some of <u>them</u> do not have bridges to the mainland. The people who live there cannot drive to work in Seattle. <u>They</u> have to take the ferryboat.
10. From Seattle you can easily get to the mountains or the seaside. <u>That</u> is why many people like living there.

Unit 3: **Building a Powerful Vocabulary**

❖ *Using pronouns*

Test 3

➤ *The pronouns in these sentences are underlined. Circle the referents.*

EXAMPLE

(Arizona) is a state in the southwestern part of the United States. <u>It</u> is located between California and New Mexico.

1. Many Native Americans live in Arizona. In the past, these people were called Indians. <u>They</u> prefer to be called "Native Americans" because <u>they</u> were, in fact, the first Americans.

2. An Indian reservation is an area of land that is kept for Native Americans. Not all Native Americans live and work on reservations. Many of <u>them</u> live outside the reservations.

3. The Native Americans living on each Indian reservation have their own special customs. The Navajos are one of the groups of Native American people. <u>They</u> have a special house with eight sides. <u>It</u> is called a "hogan."

4. The Hopi Indians are another Native American group. <u>They</u> have a reservation near the Navajos. Their land includes tall mountains with flat tops. <u>These</u> are called "mesas."

5. The capital city of Arizona is Phoenix. With a population of 1,246,712, <u>it</u> is the sixth largest city in the United States and it is growing very fast. One reason for <u>this</u> is simple: People like the hot, dry weather.

6. In Phoenix, tourists enjoy looking at the modern and Spanish-style buildings. <u>They</u> also enjoy visiting museums and eating in the many restaurants.

7. Southwestern cooking is part Mexican and part American. At the same time, <u>it</u> is very different from both Mexican and typical American cooking.

8. Tucson, Arizona, is just south of Phoenix. <u>It</u> is a smaller city than Phoenix and it does not have as many tall buildings. However, <u>it</u> has more students because it is the home of the University of Arizona.

9. Not all of Arizona is very hot. Flagstaff is a town in the northern part of the state. <u>It</u> is near high, snow-covered mountains. People go there for skiing and snowboarding.

10. In Arizona, you can visit the Grand Canyon. <u>It</u> is one of the most popular places for tourists in the United States. People travel there from all over the world. <u>They</u> say <u>it</u> is very special and very beautiful.

Unit 3: Building a Powerful Vocabulary

❖ Using synonyms

Test 1

➤ **In each passage, a word is underlined. Find and circle the synonym(s) for it in the passage.**

EXAMPLE

Natasha and Sasha lived in a small <u>village</u> for many years. They moved to Moscow this year, and they miss their (hometown.)

1. Kazu is studying medicine in Los Angeles. He likes life in the <u>western United States</u>. This part of the country has nice weather and a beautiful coast.
2. <u>Carrots, sweet potatoes, and squash</u> are very healthy for you. These vegetables are also quite tasty, and they are a good source of Vitamin A.
3. Betty was sleeping when the <u>guitar music</u> started. A lovely tune was coming from the street. She was happy to wake up to such beautiful sounds.
4. Yarek has a <u>new apartment</u> in Warsaw. He had to wait for nine years for a place to live on his own. Many people are looking for homes in Poland.
5. Sonia is studying literature at the University of <u>Bologna</u>. It is the oldest university in Europe. She is thrilled to be a student in an Italian city.
6. <u>Electronic mail</u> (e-mail) is very popular, but almost 50 percent of Americans do not use it. They think the Internet is dangerous and difficult. They prefer other ways to communicate.
7. At the Washington School, every child in the third grade learns to play the <u>violin or the flute</u>. They enjoy playing these instruments. In the future, many of the children will play in the school orchestra.
8. Anita lives in <u>Portland</u>, Oregon. This northwestern city is a very good place to ride a bicycle. There are many roads for bicycles in the downtown area.
9. <u>Lynn</u>, Massachusetts, is just 11 miles (15 kilometers) north of Boston. This city has many new Internet companies. They like to be near Boston but in a place with lower rents.
10. Nicole grows <u>roses</u> in front of her house. In the spring her front yard is full of colorful flowers. People like to walk past her house to look at her beautiful garden.

Unit 4:   Learning to Look for the Topic

Test 1

➤ *Read all the words in each group. What is the topic? Write the topic on the line. Be specific.*

EXAMPLE river lake ocean sea pond		<u>bodies of water</u>
1. dishwasher blender refrigerator toaster microwave		_____
2. cook waiter manager baker table cleaner		_____
3. whales dolphins fish shellfish sharks		_____
4. flour sugar eggs milk baking powder		_____
5. Vietnam Kampuchea Thailand Laos Singapore		_____
6. SUV jeep station wagon sedan convertible		_____
7. piano violin cello bass viola		_____
8. lettuce spinach broccoli green beans cabbage		_____
9. tent sleeping bags water bottle flashlight picnic table		_____
10. blonde black auburn gray white		_____

Name _____ Date _____

Unit 4: **Learning to Look for the Topic**

Test 2

➤ *Read all the words in each group. What is the topic? Write the topic on the line. Be specific.*

EXAMPLE   New York   San Francisco   Chicago   Seattle   Boston   ___U.S. cities___

1. Miami   Key West   Orlando   Disney World   Everglades   _____

2. menu   tables   chairs   dishes   knives and forks   _____

3. plastic   acrylic   nylon   polyester   tercel   _____

4. comma   question mark   period   semicolon   colon   _____

5. rose   daisy   lily   orchid   tulip   poppy   _____

6. balloons   songs   gifts   cake   candles   _____

7. bus   ferry   plane   taxi   train   _____

8. computer   telephone   CD player   VCR   cell phone   _____

9. water pollution   air pollution   war   sickness   floods   _____

10. running   ice-skating   skiing   swimming   rollerblading   _____

Unit 4: **Learning to Look for the Topic**

Test 3

➤ *Read all the words in each group. What is the topic? Write the topic on the line. Be specific.*

EXAMPLE	milk	cola	coffee	orange juice	tea	*drinks*

1. Tokyo   Beijing   Seoul   Taipei   Ulan Bator   _____

2. basketball   hockey   football   baseball   volleyball   _____

3. guitars   drums   electric bass   singer   amplifier   _____

4. orange   lemon   banana   grapefruit   apple   _____

5. circle   square   triangle   quadrilateral   pentagon   _____

6. mystery   romance   science fiction   horror   adventure   _____

7. coughing   sneezing   headache   fever   feeling tired   _____

8. math   history   geography   music   science   _____

9. wash the windows   sweep the floor   clean the kitchen
   wash the clothes   make the bed   _____

10. clarinet   trumpet   trombone   French horn   flute   _____

Unit 5: **Understanding Paragraphs**

❖ *Topics*

Test 1

➤ *Read each paragraph. Ask yourself, "What is it about?" Circle the correct topic. Then write "too specific" or "too general" after the other topics.*

Air Shows

1.   Air shows began in the early 1900s soon after the first plane flight. That flight happened in 1903. Orville and Wilbur Wright flew a plane for twelve seconds. A few years later, Wilbur Wright wanted to show his plane to people in New York. He flew up and down the Hudson River and hundreds of thousands of people watched him. After that, Orville and Wilbur started a flying team. There were four pilots on the team and they gave air shows in cities and towns all around the United States. Other pilots soon started flying teams and gave air shows, too.

   a. Wilbur Wright's plane   _____

   b. Airplanes in history   _____

   c. How air shows began   _____

2.   Air shows in the early days were both sport and entertainment. For the pilot, flying was a sport. In those days most pilots were men. Flying was a way for them to test their skill and their courage. For the people watching, air shows were entertainment. It was an especially exciting kind of entertainment because it was dangerous for the pilot. In fact, there were often accidents during the shows. Many of the famous early pilots lost their lives this way.

   a. Early air shows   _____

   b. The skill of early pilots   _____

   c. Airplane pilots   _____

3.   Air shows today are still a very popular kind of entertainment. The planes in these shows now are usually military planes flown by military pilots. The smaller planes do tricks in the air. They may fly upside down or in small circles. There are also groups of planes that fly very close together. The planes move apart and come together to form patterns in the air. This is very exciting to see from the ground. At these air shows, there are often planes on the ground, too. People can go into these planes and see them inside. Even today there are sometimes accidents at air shows, but they don't happen very often.

   a. Outdoor entertainment   _____

   b. Accidents at air shows   _____

   c. Air shows today   _____

Unit 5: **Understanding Paragraphs**

❖ *Topics*

Test 2

➤ *Read each paragraph. Ask yourself, "What is it about?" Circle the correct topic. Then write "too specific" or "too general" after the other topics.*

Wine

1.   People began making wine from grapes a very long time ago. There are pictures of people making wine in Egypt in about 400 B.C. The ancient Greeks and Romans made and drank wine. It was an important part of their meals and it was also important in their religions. People in Spain, France, and Germany probably learned about wine from the Romans. Wine became a part of life in many European countries. Then, after about 1500 A.D., Europeans began traveling to new continents, and they took wine with them. Soon people began making wine in North and South America, in Africa, and in Australia.

   a. The history of winemaking   _____

   b. Winemaking in Europe   _____

   c. Making wine from grapes   _____

2.   Winemaking starts with the grapes. They are usually picked at the end of the summer or in the early fall. The grapes are pressed until all the juice comes out. Then the grape juice is put into very large containers. After a few days, the juice begins to change. The sugar in the juice slowly becomes alcohol. The winemaker has to check the wine carefully every few days. Sometimes the wine has to be taken out of one container and put into another. After about six weeks, some wines are ready to drink. These are the new wines. Other wines are ready after about six months. Still others are not ready for years.

   a. When to drink wine   _____

   b. Making alcoholic drinks   _____

   c. How wine is made   _____

3. About 100 years ago, farmers in Europe were in trouble. Their grapevines (plants) for wine grapes were dying and no one understood why. Then scientists found a small insect on the roots of the grapevines. They tried different ways of killing this insect, but nothing worked. Finally, they found a way to stop it. The insect came from America. It did not kill American grapevines, so the European farmers decided to plant the roots of American grapevines. Then they could grow their grapes from these roots. It took many years to change the roots of all the grapevines in Europe. And that is how the wines of Europe were saved.

a. Grapevines in Europe   _____

b. How European wines were saved   _____

c. How European farmers planted new roots _____

Unit 5: **Understanding Paragraphs**

❖ *Topics*

Test 3

➤ *Read each paragraph. Ask yourself, "What is it about?" Then write the topic after the paragraph.*

Firefighting

1.   Firefighters in New York do not have an easy job. In fact, they have to do many different things, not just fight fires. They have to be good drivers so they can drive the fire truck fast through busy streets. At the fire, they have to decide quickly what to do. Then they have to work hard to put out the fire and save people in danger. Sometimes, they may be in danger themselves, but they cannot show fear. After the fire is out, firefighters often help find the cause of the fire. Later, they return to the firehouse. There, they clean and fix the fire truck so it will be ready for the next fire.

Topic: _____

2.   Every year in the United States there are hundreds of forest fires. Thousands of firefighters work to stop these fires. They have special water trucks and firefighting planes and helicopters. In normal conditions, they can usually stop most forest fires and save the trees and animals there. Sometimes it is not possible to stop the fire. The most dangerous fires happen when the forest is very dry. Then, if there is also wind, the fire moves more quickly. It can even jump across roads or rivers. In fact, it is almost impossible to stop a fire in a dry forest with a lot of wind. The firefighters have to wait for a change in the weather.

Topic: _____

3.   The best way to fight fires is not to start them. There are a few simple rules to follow about fires. In the house, you should not leave anything—a rug or a curtain—close to the fireplace. Never leave the house with any kind of fire burning. Even a very small fire can be dangerous. Candles and cigarettes, for example, cause many house fires. Outside of the house, you should also be careful. Never start a fire in a dry forest or under a tree. In your yard, make sure a fire is far away from anything that could burn. Stay with the fire until it goes out.

Topic: _____

Unit 5: **Understanding Paragraphs**

❖ *Topics*

Test 4

➤ *Read each paragraph. Ask yourself, "What is it about?" Then write the topic after the paragraph.*

Farming

1.   Farming in the United States today is very different from farming 100 years ago. In those days, farmers did not have many machines to help them. They had animals—horses or oxen. But animals work slowly compared to machines. This meant that farms were smaller than they are now. Farmers also worked in a different way in the past. In those days, farmers had to feed their families. They grew fruit and vegetables and kept cows, pigs, sheep, and chickens. Modern farmers do not have to feed their families. They can buy food at the supermarket. Today farmers grow things on the farm so they can sell them.

Topic: _____

2.   Farming is not just a job. It is a way of life. In many ways farmers have a very special life. First of all, they cannot leave the job at the end of the day. They live on the farm and there is always work to do. Second, a lot of farm work is outdoors, so the weather is very important for farmers. It is also important for the success of their farms. A lot of bad weather means farmers will lose money. Finally, farmers work with plants and animals. They understand nature better than other people do.

Topic: _____

3.   Farm work changes with the seasons. The spring is planting time. Farmers are very busy getting the fields ready and then planting the seeds. In the summer, farmers must watch the plants carefully. Some may need water. Other plants may have problems with insects or diseases. Then in the summer or in the fall, the fruits or plants are ready for picking. That is a very busy time for farmers. The winter is a time for rest or for work on the farm machines.

Topic: _____

Unit 5: **Understanding Paragraphs**

❖ *Main ideas*

Test 1

➤ *Read each paragraph. Ask yourself, "What is the topic? What is the writer's idea about the topic?" Choose the best main-idea statement by circling the letter in front of it.*

Mushrooms

1.   When people think of mushrooms, they usually think of one kind. This is the kind you see in pictures and read about in stories. It has a white bottom and a red top. However, mushrooms can be found in many different sizes, shapes, and colors. Some mushrooms are very small. They are so small you cannot even see them with just your eye. Other mushrooms are very, very large. For example, one mushroom that grows underground can be the size of a football field. There are mushrooms that look like big balls and mushrooms that look like sticks. Some are white, others are yellow, orange, brown, black, or even purple.

   a. There are mushrooms in many countries around the world.

   b. The mushrooms in stories are white and red.

   c. There are many different sizes, shapes, and colors of mushrooms.

2.   Mushrooms look like plants, but they are not plants. Plants make their own food from water and sunlight. Mushrooms cannot make their own food. They need to get their food from somewhere else. Mushrooms usually find their food in plants, especially dead plants. In fact, you usually find mushrooms on dead leaves or wood. In one way, however, mushrooms are like plants. They have a kind of seed. This seed, called a spore, falls from the mushroom. It may be blown far away by the wind, or it may fall straight down. When it lands on the ground, another mushroom grows there.

   a. Mushrooms are both different from and similar to plants.

   b. Mushrooms grow on dead leaves or wood.

   c. Mushrooms are like plants because they have seeds called spores.

3.   Many people go looking for mushrooms in the forest. Some of these people want to find mushrooms to eat. All around the world, people love to cook and eat wild mushrooms. You have to be very careful about wild mushrooms, however. Many kinds of mushrooms are not good to eat. They may even make you sick. People also look for mushrooms for other reasons. Scientists want to find mushrooms so they can study them and understand them better. Some people are just interested in seeing mushrooms where they grow. Some even like to photograph them.

a. You can find many different kinds of mushrooms.

b. Some people like to cook and eat wild mushrooms.

c. People look for mushrooms for several reasons.

Unit 5: **Understanding Paragraphs**

❖ *Main ideas*

Test 2

➤ *Read each paragraph. Ask yourself, "What is the topic? What is the writer's idea about the topic?" Choose the best main-idea statement by circling the letter in front of it.*

The Rights of Black Americans

1.   In the early 1950s, black Americans and white Americans usually lived in different parts of town. They sent their children to different schools. In the southern states, the state laws kept blacks and whites separate in all public places. Restaurants did not let black people enter. Blacks had to sit in the back of the churches and the theaters. They also had to sit in the back of the buses or stand up if a white person wanted a seat in the back.

  a. Black Americans lived separately from whites in the 1950s.

  b. Many black Americans lived in the southern states in the 1950s.

  c. Blacks could not go into some restaurants in the 1950s.

2.   Rosa Parks was a black woman who lived in Montgomery, Alabama, a city in the southern United States. On December 5, 1955, she was very tired after working all day. A white person wanted her seat on the bus, but she refused to stand up. Because of that, she was arrested and put in jail. The black people in Montgomery were very angry. They decided to stop riding the buses. Dr. Martin Luther King, Jr., became their leader. He organized public meetings and gave many speeches. People around the country began to talk about the problems in the south. Finally, after more than a year, the law was changed. Separate seating on buses and in other public places was not allowed any more.

  a. Black Americans did not have many rights in the southern United States.

  b. Rosa Parks and Martin Luther King were black Americans.

  c. American blacks succeeded in changing the laws about separate seating.

3.   In the early 1960s, Dr. King led another important battle for American blacks. He helped them win the right to vote. The fight for the vote began in Selma, Alabama. This town had a large population of blacks, but local laws allowed only 2 percent of them to vote. Dr. King began to organize meetings and marches from Selma to Montgomery, the state capital. The marchers were peaceful, but the police and some other white people were not. Many marchers were hurt or went to jail and several people died. Finally, in 1965, the United States government made a new law. It gave all Americans, of every color, the right to vote.

a. In the 1960s, Dr. King organized marches and meetings.

b. In the 1960s, all Americans won the right to vote.

c. In the 1960s, not all Americans wanted to vote.

Unit 5: Understanding Paragraphs

❖ **Main ideas**

Test 3

➤ **Read each paragraph. Ask yourself, "What is the topic? What is the writer's idea about the topic?" Then write a main-idea statement.**

The Plant Medicines of Madagascar

1.   Madagascar is a large island off the southeast coast of Africa. It is always warm there and it rains often. Many special plants can grow in that climate. Some of these plants do not grow anywhere else in the world. One example is the rosy periwinkle. It is a small green plant with a white and pink flower. People in Madagascar use it as a medicine. Scientists studied the rosy periwinkle. They learned that, in fact, it is a very good medicine. Doctors now use it to fight serious disease.

   Main idea: _____

   _____

2.   In Madagascar, there are few hospitals and not many doctors. People with health problems usually go to the local healer. These healers listen to their patients. Then they decide on the best medicine. All the medicines are made from plants from the forests. Some are made from the flowers. Others are made from the leaves or the roots. Sometimes, with serious diseases, such as malaria, these plant medicines do not work. Very often, however, they do solve the problem.

   Main idea: _____

   _____

3.   The plant medicines of Madagascar may be able to help doctors around the world. Some of these plants are already used in modern medicine. Many others could be useful. But doctors do not understand the plants very well. They do not always know why the plants work as medicine. Scientists are trying to learn more about the plants in Madagascar. They are studying the forests where the plants grow. They are talking with the healers and watching them work. They hope to learn how to grow the plants and how to make medicines from them.

   Main idea: _____

   _____

Unit 5: **Understanding Paragraphs**

❖ *Main ideas*

Test 4

➤ *Read each paragraph. Ask yourself, "What is the topic? What is the writer's idea about the topic?" Then write a main-idea statement.*

Water

1. People who live in the United States use much more water than people in any other country. They use a lot of water in the washing machines and dishwashers in their homes. They also use water for their gardens and to wash their cars. Most Americans take long showers or deep baths everyday. Sometimes they let water run in the sink. They don't turn it off when they don't need it. Americans rarely think about water when they use it. They think there will always be enough.

    Main idea: _____

    _____

2. In many African countries, water is a problem. It does not rain much in these countries, so there is never very much water. In the past, there was usually enough water for all the people, but now there are many more people. More people need more water. Farmers are using more and more water to grow food. Companies are using more water for factories. People are using more water for drinking, cooking, and washing. The result is simple: not enough water. Some African countries already do not have enough water for everyone. Others will soon be in trouble.

    Main idea: _____

    _____

3. Some countries have a lot of water. Canada, for example, has 40 percent of the world's supply of fresh (not salty) water. People in Canada and other countries with a lot of water do not think much about their water. However, some day they may be able to sell their water to other countries. They will have to find a way to ship it to other parts of the world. That will not be easy and it will be expensive. In fact, some people believe that water could become very expensive some day, like oil. The countries with a lot of water could then become very rich.

    Main idea: _____

    _____

Unit 6: **Finding the Pattern of Organization**

❖ *Listing pattern*

Test 1

➤ *Read each paragraph and underline the signal words. Write the topic and main idea. Then write the signal words and details.*

A New Kind of Car in the United States

1. The sports utility vehicle (SUV) was invented in the early 1990s. It quickly became very popular in the United States. There are several reasons for this. First of all, it is larger than most cars. It can carry lots of people, bicycles, toys, dogs, and other things. This makes it popular with families. It also has four doors and a big back door, so getting in or out is easy. In addition, an SUV is taller than most cars. This means that the driver can see above other cars and can see the road well. Finally, an SUV has a lot more power than most cars, so it can go faster. It can also go on very rough roads where other cars cannot go.

Topic: _____

Main idea: _____

_____

Signal Words   Details

_____   _____

_____   _____

_____   _____

_____   _____

_____   _____

2. The SUV is popular with many people, but other people do not like these cars. First, these cars are larger than most other cars. This means that drivers of other cars may not be able to see the road well. Also, SUVs are very heavy. If an SUV gets into an accident with a small car, the small car may be in serious trouble. Another problem with SUVs is that they are very expensive.

They are expensive to buy—about 50 percent more expensive than an average small car. They are also expensive to use, since they use a lot more gasoline than smaller cars. For example, a small car uses about one U.S. gallon (3.8 liters) to go about 40 miles (64 kilometers). An SUV, however, can go only about 15 miles on the same amount of gasoline.

Topic: _____

Main idea: _____

_____

Signal Words	Details
_____	_____
_____	_____
_____	_____

3.   There are two ways to solve the problems caused by SUVs. One way is to change the way we think about them. Now they are sold as large cars. In the future, maybe they should be sold as trucks. Then people with just a car license could not drive them. They would have to get a truck license. These licenses are more expensive and difficult to get, so probably fewer people would buy SUVs. Another way to solve SUV problems is to make them differently. Some people think that car companies should make big SUVs smaller and less dangerous. They should also make SUVs with less powerful engines. Then they would not use so much gasoline.

Topic: _____

Main idea: _____

_____

Signal Words	Details
_____	_____
_____	_____

Unit 6: **Finding the Pattern of Organization**

❖ *Time order pattern*

Test 1

➤ *Read each paragraph and underline the signal words. Write the topic and main idea. Then write the signal words and details.*

The Williams Sisters—Tennis Champions

1.   Venus and Serena Williams are the youngest of five daughters in the Williams family. They were born in 1980 and 1982. By the age of four, they were already playing tennis. They practiced with their father in their hometown of Compton, California. When they were still very young, Venus and Serena began to play in tennis tournaments. They played in and won many junior tournaments in southern California. Then, in 1991, their father made two important decisions. He decided that his daughters should not play in junior tournaments. They should play in adult tournaments. He also decided to send the girls to work with a tennis teacher in Florida. This was the beginning of their tennis career.

Topic: _____

Main idea: _____

_____

Signal Words   *Details*

_____   _____

_____   _____

_____   _____

_____   _____

2.   Venus and Serena became famous tennis players when they were still teenagers. During those years, they worked hard on their tennis skills. In 1993, the Williams family moved to Florida so they could be closer to their daughters. That year, the girls began to earn money for their tennis playing. A sports clothing company paid the girls to wear certain clothes. They became professional tennis players in 1995. Venus was fifteen and Serena only thirteen. By 1998, both Venus and Serena were among the top ten tennis players in the world. In 1999, they had to play each other in an Australian

tournament. Venus won, but the sisters were still friends. They practiced together and often played together in doubles tournaments.

Topic: _____

Main idea: _____

_____

Signal Words   *Details*

_____   _____

_____   _____

_____   _____

_____   _____

3.   The years 1999 and 2000 were very good years for the Williams sisters. On September 11, 1999, Serena won the U.S. Open Tennis Tournament. The prize for winning the tournament was $750,000. Even more important, she was the first African-American woman to win since 1958. The next day, Serena played with Venus as a team and they won the doubles tournament. Then, in July 2000, Serena and Venus competed against one another at Wimbledon, England, the most famous tennis tournament in the world. This time Venus won the game and went on to win the tournament. At Wimbledon, they also played doubles together, and again they won the doubles tournament.

Topic: _____

Main idea: _____

_____

Signal Words   *Details*

_____   _____

_____   _____

_____   _____

                            _____

Unit 6: **Finding the Pattern of Organization**

❖ *Cause-and-effect pattern*

Test 1

➤ *Read each paragraph. Underline the signal words. Write the main idea of the paragraph. Write the causes and the effects on the lines after the main idea.*

Deserts Around the World

1.   In a desert, very little rain falls, usually less than 254 millimeters (10 inches) in a year. Most deserts are very hot during the day and cold at night. As a result, only some special animals and plants can live in the desert. Many desert animals sleep underground during the heat of the day and go out only at night. Other desert animals sleep for many months and wake up only when it rains. Dry desert weather also leads to special kinds of plants. Some desert plants live only for a few days. Their seeds stay a long time on the dry ground, sometimes for years. Then when it rains, they quickly grow and flower.

Topic: _____

Main idea: _____

Causes   Effects

_____   _____

_____   _____

                                       _____

2.   People can change desert land into farmland by irrigation (adding water). The water comes from wells deep underground. However, irrigation can lead to serious problems. One bad effect of irrigation is using up all the underground water. Then the desert land becomes even drier. Another effect of irrigation is that it changes the soil. After many years of irrigation, the soil has lots of salt and minerals in it. As a result, plants will not grow there any more.

Topic: _____

Main idea: _____

Causes   *Effects*

_____   _____

                          _____

                          _____

                          _____

3. Many of the world's deserts are growing larger. There are two reasons for this. One reason is that more people are living near deserts and they are changing the land. These people often keep animals for meat or milk. The animals eat all the grass and small plants. At the same time, people cut down the trees for firewood. Then there are no plants to hold the soil and it can blow away with the wind. The other reason for larger deserts is the changing weather. These days, the weather in some desert areas is hotter and drier. This makes it even harder for plants and trees to grow again.

Topic: _____

Main idea: _____

Causes   *Effects*

_____   _____

_____   _____

                          _____

Unit 6: **Finding the Pattern of Organization**

❖ *Comparison pattern*

Test 1

➤ *Read each paragraph and underline the signal words. Answer the question following the paragraph. Then write the main idea, likeness(es), and difference(s) on the lines after the question.*

Australia and the United States

1.   From the 1600s to the 1800s, ships left England for many parts of the world, including North America and Australia. These ships were often full of people. The people who went to North America, however, were very different from the people who went to Australia. The people going to North America wanted to leave England. They were looking for freedom of religion and a new life. The people going to Australia did not want to leave England. They were sent away from the country because they were criminals. In fact, from 1780 to 1850 Great Britain used Australia like a jail.

What is this paragraph comparing? _____

Main idea: _____

_____

Likeness   *Differences*

_____   _____

                                                  _____

                                                  _____

2.   The history of the native people in Australia and North America is similar. When the first Europeans arrived in both places, they found other people already there. In Australia, these people are called Aborigines. Similarly, the English found people in North America and called them Indians. These people are now called Native Americans. In both Australia and North America, the English fought and killed many native people. They also took away their land and took away all their power. In fact, the native people of both Australia and the United States did not start to vote in national elections until the 1960s.

What is this paragraph comparing? _____

Main idea: _____

_____

Likenesses

_____

_____

_____

_____

3.   In size, Australia is almost as large as the United States. However, in most ways the two countries are very different. The population of Australia is about 19 million, while the population of the United States is about 270 million. The governments of the two countries are also different. The United States fought a war against Great Britain and is not part of Britain any more. Australia, however, is still part of the British Commonwealth. The countries are also different in geography. Australia's land is almost two-thirds desert and there are very few rivers. In the United States, however, the desert area is a very small part of the country, and there are many rivers and lakes.

What is this paragraph comparing? _____

Main idea: _____

_____

Likeness

_____

Differences

_____

_____

_____

Unit 6: **Finding the Pattern of Organization**

❖ *Using all four patterns*

Test 1

➤ *In each of the following paragraphs, there is a missing sentence and a different pattern. The missing sentences (plus one extra sentence) and the patterns are listed in the box following the paragraphs. After each paragraph, write the letter of the missing sentence and the pattern.*

The California Gold Rush

1. In January 1848, James Marshall and John Sutter were building a mill in the hills of the Sacramento Valley in California. Marshall found some gold in the Sacramento River. _____ A few days later, the Sacramento River was full of boats carrying people from San Francisco to look for gold. In the next few months, news about the gold traveled quickly across the country. By January of 1849, people were coming to California from all over the United States and from other countries, too.

    Sentence _____   *Pattern* _____

2. About 100,000 people, mostly men, took part in the Gold Rush of 1849. They made the long trip to California in several different ways. Some people went by boat to Panama in South America. Then they took a horse and wagon across Panama and took another boat to San Francisco. _____ This was a long, dangerous and expensive way to travel. Many others traveled all the way across North America by horse and wagon. This was less expensive, but it was a very long, difficult, and dangerous trip.

    Sentence _____   *Pattern* _____

3. There are two ways to find gold. The easiest way is to find it in rivers. This is how Marshall found his gold. River gold is mixed with small, dirty stones. The gold is dirty, too, so you usually do not see it at first. _____ The other way to find gold is by digging underground. This is much more difficult and dangerous. Workers dig a deep hole in the ground. Then they go down into the hole and dig out rocks with gold in them. Strong chemicals are used to get the gold from the rocks.

    Sentence _____   *Pattern* _____

4.   The Gold Rush led to big changes in California. The biggest change was in the population. In a very short time, new towns were started and small towns became cities. San Francisco, for example, grew from a town of 200 to a city of 50,000 in eight years. The people who moved to California, which became known as the "Golden State," all had a dream. They believed that if they could find gold, they could get rich quickly. _____

Sentence _____   *Pattern* _____

Missing Sentences

a. Others made a longer sea trip all the way around South America.

b. That spring, a neighbor went to San Francisco and told people there about the gold.

c. In fact, people began to think of California as a place where anything could happen.

d. The gold miners lived in tiny houses made of cloth and old pieces of wood.

e. However, you can wash the stones in the river and then you can see the gold.

Patterns

L—listing   **TO**—time order   **CE**—cause and effect   **C**—Comparison

---

Unit 6: **Finding the Pattern of Organization**

❖ *Using all four patterns*

Test 2

➤ *In each of the following paragraphs, there is a missing sentence and a different pattern. The missing sentences (plus one extra sentence) and the patterns are listed in the box following the paragraphs. After each paragraph, write the letter of the missing sentence and the pattern.*

The Harry Potter Books

1.   In 1990 J. K. Rowling lived with her young daughter in Edinburgh, Scotland. She worked as a part-time teacher, but she wanted to write a book. One day she had an idea for a children's book. _____ She made many notes and read lots of books. Finally, she started writing. Her first book, *Harry Potter and the Philosopher's Stone* (or *Harry Potter and the Sorcerer's Stone*) was published in 1997. It was a big success right from the beginning. After that, she wrote more books about Harry Potter. By 2001, she was one of the most successful writers in the world.

   Sentence _____   *Pattern* _____

2.   There is a very good reason for the success of the Harry Potter books. The reason is that children love the special kind of magic in these stories. They like to read about flying on a broom and wearing special clothes so no one can see them. They like to think that there are magic ways to learn how to walk through a wall. _____ In fact, he and his friends seem very real and many of their problems are the kinds of problems children have in their own lives.

   Sentence _____   *Pattern* _____

3.   J. K. Rowling, the author of the Harry Potter books, is setting a lot of records. First of all, she is now earning more money from her books than any other writer. In three years, she earned more than $30 million. _____ That book had the biggest first printing ever. In just the United States, 3,800,000 books were printed. Millions more were printed in Great Britain and other countries. Finally, Rowling is the first author to have so many books on the New York Times best-seller list. At one time, her first four books were all at the top of the list.

   Sentence _____   *Pattern* _____

4.   The Harry Potter stories are like traditional fairy tales in some ways. There is a hero—Harry—and there is a bad guy. Like the heroes of fairy tales, Harry has many dangerous adventures. Like fairy tales, the stories about Harry always have a happy ending. However, in some ways these stories are not like fairy tales at all. Unlike traditional tales, the Harry Potter stories are about the present day, not about long ago. _____

Harry and his friends come from families that live just like any other family.

Sentence _____   *Pattern* _____

Missing Sentences

a. They also like the happy ending of every story and they like Harry a lot.

b. There are no kings and princesses in Harry's life, either.

c. She thought about the idea for several years.

d. The *New York Times* published many reviews of children's books.

e. Her fourth book, *The Goblet of Fire,* also set a record.

Patterns

L—listing   **TO**—time order   **CE**—cause and effect   **C**—Comparison

---

Unit 7:   **Making Inferences**

❖ *Inferences from conversations*

Test 1

➤ *Read the conversations and answer the questions that follow.*

1. A: This is not working out at all.
   B: What are you going to do?
   A: I guess I'll have to take it back.
   B: Can you do that?
   A: Yes. They said I had a week to try it out.
   B: Are you going to get something else?
   A: No way. I want my money back.
   B: What about a bird or a fish or something like that? They don't make messes or destroy the furniture.
   A: They're no fun, either.
   B: Well, you can't have everything.

   1. What are these people talking about? _____

   2. Where are they? _____

2. A: Are you sure that's a good idea?
   B: Why not?
   A: A lot of people don't eat red meat these days.
   B: Is John a vegetarian?
   A: I'm not sure, but he might be.
   B: But I've already got the steaks! What do we do with them?
   A: Put them in the freezer.
   B: What do we cook instead?
   A: What about rice with vegetables? We've got everything we need, don't we?
   B: Oh, all right. But you can cook. I'm not so good at things like that.

   1. What are these people talking about? _____

   2. Where are they? _____

Unit 7: **Making Inferences**

❖ *Inferences from conversations*

Test 2

➤ *Read the conversations and answer the questions that follow.*

1. A: I heard someone say she's from Italy.
   B: Italy! She doesn't look like she's from Italy.
   A: How do you know? Ever been there?
   B: No, but she looks . . .
   A: She's very good-looking.
   B: She sure is.
   A: Let's go talk to her.
   B: Are you kidding? She won't want to talk to us!
   A: She might want to meet some second-year students.
   B: You think so?
   A: Yeah, and we'd better get over there fast before some other guy does.
   B: Too late. Look, she's talking to Jack Summers.

   1. What are these people talking about? _____

   2. Where are they? _____

2. A: I'm the person who called this morning.
   B: Oh, yes. Come in. Let me get the keys. This way. It's just across the hall.
   A: Hmm. Big enough for me. There's lots of light. What about parking?
   B: You can park in the street. It's never a problem.
   A: The heat?
   B: It's oil heat and it's included in the rent.
   A: Great. Oh, one last question. You don't mind dogs, do you?
   B: Sorry, no pets.
   A: But he's a very small dog and he won't be any trouble.
   B: I'm afraid I have to say no. We had a terrible time with a dog once.
   A: That's too bad.

   1. What are these people talking about? _____

   2. Where are they? _____

Unit 7:   Making Inferences

❖ Inferences from stories

Test 1

➤ **Read this passage from The Lady in the Lake, *a book by Raymond Chandler, retold by Jennifer Bassett. Answer the questions and underline the words or phrases that helped you.***

In his quiet, expensive office Derace Kingsley listened to me with a white face.
"Did your wife have a gun?" I asked.
"Yes."
"Is this it?" I showed him the gun from the floor in Lavery's bathroom.
5 He looked at it, and then at me. "I don't know. Perhaps. But Crystal isn't a murderer—she didn't kill Lavery."
"Why not? The police are going to think she did. She was with Lavery in San Bernardino. They didn't go to Mexico. Then perhaps one day she sees him with another woman. So she gets angry, and goes round to his house. She leaves the gun
10 on the floor, her dress in the cupboard. . . . The police are going to love it." I stood up and looked down at him. "I must take the gun back now and call the police. I can't cover up a murder."
Kingsley said nothing and put his head in his hands. Then he looked up at me. "Listen, Marlowe," he said quietly. "You're working for me, right? I *know* Crystal
15 didn't kill Lavery! What about that woman in the blue hat? Who was she? Lavery knew a lot of women. Go and find the murderer. Show the police that Crystal didn't kill Lavery. Do that, and there's $500 for you."
"OK, Mr. Kingsley," I said. "But the job gets more difficult every day."

1. Who is the narrator of the story? _____

2. What is the narrator's job? _____

3. Who are the other people in the story? _____

4. What happened before this passage in the story? _____

5. What do you think will happen next? _____

Unit 7:   **Making Inferences**

❖ *Inferences from stories*

Test 2

➤ *Read this passage from* **The Mysterious Island,** *by Jules Verne, retold by D. K. Swan. Answer the questions and underline the words or phrases that helped you.*

They looked 'round them.

"There seem to be plenty of trees," said Spillet. "And I saw hills, so there are probably streams with fresh water coming down from them. I want to climb a hill and look at the island. We must know if there are people and houses anywhere. Will
5 you two walk along the shore and look for food and water? We'll meet again here before the sun goes down."

Pencroft and Herbert, the boy, walked along the beach to the south. They had not gone far when Pencroft said: "Those rocks by the edge of the water will make a very good house for us. And there's a little stream just beyond them. That will bring
10 fresh water. There'll be food on the rocks, too."

"Food?" said Herbert. "I can see rocks for a house and a stream for water, but where's the food?"

"It'll be on the rocks. I've been round the world, you know, and there are always shellfish on rocks like those."

15 Herbert saw another difficulty.

"We can't eat these shellfish without cooking them, and we haven't got a fire."

The sailor felt in his pockets, but his box of matches had gone.

"Perhaps the others have some matches," he said. "Let's go and get wood for a fire and the branches of trees for a roof and a door to finish our rock house."

20 They went among the trees. Herbert found some eggs and Pencroft found dead wood for a fire and the best branches for the house. They took all these things to the rock, and then it was time to meet Spillet.

1. Who are the characters in the story? _____

2. Where are they? _____

3. Why are they there? _____

4. What are the people in the story trying to do? _____

5. What do you think will happen next? _____

Unit 8: **Skimming**

❖ *Skimming for point of view*

Test 1

➤ *Read these paragraphs quickly. Ask yourself, "Is the writer for or against the idea?" Put a checkmark (✓) beside the answer. Time limit: 2 minutes.*

1. Pets can help older people in many ways. Many older people live alone, so a pet is good company. Pets also show their love and older people need this love. Doctors also say that pets help people stay healthy.

    For _____ *Against* _____

2. Some American families do not send their children to school. The children learn at home. This sometimes causes problems for the children. They may not learn how to play with other children. They also may not have very many friends.

    For _____ *Against* _____

3. All new cars today have seat belts. They can save your life in an accident. So when you get in your car, you should always put on your seat belt!

    For _____ *Against* _____

4. Swimming in the ocean is not always safe. The water may be polluted and dirty. There may be high waves that can pull you under water. Sometimes there are even dangerous fish or sharks that could hurt you.

    For _____ *Against* _____

5. Travel by train is much more relaxing than travel by car. In a train, you do not have to watch the road. You can read a book, sleep, or eat a meal. You can also get up and move around when you want.

    For _____ *Against* _____

6. There are several important reasons for learning to play the piano. Children who take piano lessons do better at school. Later in life, these children will enjoy music more. They can also continue to play piano as a hobby or with friends.

    For _____ *Against* _____

7.   Too much fast food is harmful to your health. These foods are full of fat, salt, and sugar. They may also have lots of chemicals in them. So if you want to be healthy, stay away from fast foods.

For _____   *Against* _____

8.   Many people now carry cellular phones with them all the time. These phones make life easier. You can use them to call someone if you are late. You can also call a doctor or the police in an emergency.

For _____   *Against* _____

Unit 8: **Skimming**

❖ *Skimming for pattern of organization*

Test 1

➤ *Read each of these paragraphs quickly. Read only to find the pattern of organization. Put a checkmark (✓) next to the best answer. Time limit: 2 minutes.*

1.   In the past, people could travel between Sweden and Denmark only by boat. Now there is a new bridge and tunnel between the two countries, and you can travel by car. The trip is much faster these days. Before, it took 45 minutes, but now it takes only 15 minutes.

   Listing _____   *Time order* _____   *Cause/effect* _____   *Comparison* _____

2.   High school students in the United States carry many electronic items in their book bags these days. They usually have a portable phone, a calculator, and a beeper. Some students also carry a compact disk player and an electronic dictionary.

   Listing _____   *Time order* _____   *Cause/effect* _____   *Comparison* _____

3.   Carol's accident happened in part because of the weather. It was a dark and stormy night, so she could not see the road well. But there was another reason for the accident. Carol was talking on her cell phone and she was not watching the road carefully.

   Listing _____   *Time order* _____   *Cause/effect* _____   *Comparison* _____

4.   The Galileo spaceship, was sent into space in October 1989 to study the planet Jupiter. Two years later, Galileo was halfway to Jupiter. In December 1995, Galileo reached Jupiter and began to circle the planet.

   Listing _____   *Time order* _____   *Cause/effect* _____   *Comparison* _____

5.   The little girls are twins, but they do not look alike. Piper is not as tall as Anna. Anna has large eyes and dark brown hair, while Piper has smaller eyes and light, golden hair. But both girls have beautiful smiles.

   Listing _____   *Time order* _____   *Cause/effect* _____   *Comparison* _____

6.   The hot weather caused some serious problems in the western United States last summer. It made the forests very dry and that led to forest fires. The high temperatures also caused other kinds of problems. People needed to use their air conditioners more, so sometimes there was not enough electricity.

Listing _____   *Time order* _____   *Cause/effect* _____   *Comparison* _____

7.   Learning English in Australia is very different from learning English in Spain. In Australia, students can hear and practice English outside class. But in Spain, students hear English only in the classroom.

Listing _____   *Time order* _____   *Cause/effect* _____   *Comparison* _____

8.   The Boston Red Sox baseball team needs a new baseball stadium for several reasons. First, the old stadium was built more than ninety years ago and it has many problems. Second, it is too small. Many baseball fans cannot get tickets for baseball games.

Listing _____   *Time order* _____   *Cause/effect* _____   *Comparison* _____

Unit 8: **Skimming**

❖ ***Skimming for pattern of organization***

Test 2

➤ ***Read each of these paragraphs quickly. Read only to find the pattern of organization. Put a checkmark (✓) next to the best answer. Time limit: 2 minutes.***

1. In Los Angeles, California, there are 4 million cars on the roads every day. All these cars mean that there are many accidents and there is terrible air pollution. The cars also lead to another problem: slow travel time. At busy times, the cars move at only about 17 miles (27 kilometers) per hour.

    Listing _____   *Time order* _____   *Cause/effect* _____   *Comparison* _____

2. The Galileo spaceship, which is close to the moons of the planet Jupiter, is sending scientists on Earth lots of new information. For example, scientists now know that one of the moons has a volcano. They also know that there is water on another moon.

    Listing _____   *Time order* _____   *Cause/effect* _____   *Comparison* _____

3. Abraham Lincoln's life in politics began in 1832. He ran for a seat in the Illinois House of Representatives. He did not win that election, but he ran again in 1834. This time he won. Then, in 1846, he won election to the U.S. Congress. And finally, in 1860, Lincoln won the election for United States President.

    Listing _____   *Time order* _____   *Cause/effect* _____   *Comparison* _____

4. Stephen King, an American author, is one of the world's most successful living writers. His books include thirty-four novels and eight collections of short stories. His work also includes five plays for television and five plays that were made into movies. His latest two books were published on the Internet.

    Listing _____   *Time order* _____   *Cause/effect* _____   *Comparison* _____

5. More people die of heart attacks on Monday than on any other day. Scottish doctors think they know the reason why. Some people drink extra alcohol on the weekend. This extra alcohol could be the cause of the heart attacks.

    Listing _____   *Time order* _____   *Cause/effect* _____   *Comparison* _____

6.   In the 1920s, movies were black and white, with no sound. In the 1930s, movies were made with sound, including the voices of the actors. In the 1940s, movie producers started making color movies. Starting in the 1980s, some films were made with the help of computers. Who knows what the 2000s will bring?

Listing _____   *Time order* _____   *Cause/effect* _____   *Comparison* _____

7.   Many problems faced the people who traveled across North America to California. Sometimes rainstorms flooded the southern trails. After the rainstorms, thousands of travelers died of cholera, a terrible sickness. On the mountain trails, snowstorms blocked trails and the cold killed many travelers.

Listing _____   *Time order* _____   *Cause/effect* _____   *Comparison* _____

8.   Europeans and Americans generally have different ideas about food. Many Europeans are very interested in the food they eat. They want food of the highest quality. Americans, on the other hand, often eat "junk food." To Americans, food is often just something to fill their stomachs.

Listing _____   *Time order* _____   *Cause/effect* _____   *Comparison* _____

Unit 8: **Skimming**

❖ *Skimming for ideas*

Test 1

➤ *Skim the following review as quickly as possible for the general ideas about the book. Remember, you need to read only a few sentences and words. Then answer the questions that follow. Time limit: 4 minutes.*

NOTHING LIKE IT IN THE WORLD

The Men Who Built the Transcontinental Railroad, 1863–1869

by Stephen E. Ambrose   *Reviewed by Winona Green*

The railroad across the United States was built between 1863 and 1869. The 2,000-mile train track changed the history of North America. It tied the older cities in the East to the new cities in the West. Now people could travel by train instead of by horse and wagon. Train travel was much faster, easier, and safer. Companies could also use the railroad to send food, clothes, and other things to the West.

This is not the first book about building the railroad across the United States. There are already several books on this subject. Some are longer and some have more information. But Ambrose writes a good story, and that makes his book better than the others.

In this book, Ambrose writes about the two railroad companies and the people in the railroad business. The most interesting parts of the book, however, are about the railroad workers. Thousands of workers from all parts of the world built the railroad. Ambrose tells their story well. There were few machines to help them. Their work was very hard and sometimes dangerous. In fact, many workers lost their lives while working on the railroad.

Nothing Like It in the World is a good history book. It is easy to read. It is also full of important information. Readers will enjoy the maps and photographs. There are many pictures of the railroad workers and a famous photograph taken on the day the railroad was finished.

1. This book is about
   a. travel in the United States.
   b. building a railroad.
   c. people who travel on trains.

2. The transcontinental railroad
   a. was easy to build.
   b. did not change anything for Americans.
   c. made a difference in American history.

3. The railroad workers
   a. came mostly from the west.
   b. had a hard life.
   c. lived on trains.

4. Does the reviewer think this is a good book? _____

   How do you know? List some key words here: _____

   _____

Name _____ Date _____

Unit 8: **Skimming**

❖ *Skimming for ideas*

Test 2

➤ *Skim the following review as quickly as possible for the general ideas about the book. Remember, you need to read only a few sentences and words. Then answer the questions that follow. Time limit: 4 minutes.*

EINSTEIN IN LOVE

A Scientific Romance

by Dennis Overbye   *Reviewed by Ralph Green*

Everyone knows about Albert Einstein, the famous scientist. His work in physics was very important. Until recently, however, there was little information about Einstein as a person. Then, about ten years ago, someone found a few boxes of letters written by Einstein. These were not letters to scientists about his work. They were letters to Einstein's wives and family.

Dennis Overbye uses information from the letters in his new book about Einstein. The book tells about Einstein's life up to age forty. It shows how his marriages and his personal life were important to his work.

Some people believe that Einstein did his best work when he was happily in love. In this book, however, Overbye shows that this was not true. In fact,

Einstein did great work when his love life was unhappy. The book describes Einstein's first marriage. It was not a happy one. During that time, Einstein wrote his first great scientific papers, including the one with the famous formula: $E = mc^2$.

After ten years of marriage, Einstein divorced his wife and immediately married another woman. However, that marriage was also unhappy. At that time, Einstein wrote another very important paper about physics and astronomy.

Readers will enjoy this book about Einstein. It shows how Einstein's personal life and his scientific work belonged to one man. It shows him as a real person, with both a brain and a heart.

1. This book is about
   a. Einstein's scientific work.
   b. Einstein's family.
   c. Einstein as a person.

2. Overbye found information about Einstein's life in his
   a. letters.
   b. books.
   c. scientific papers.

3. Overbye thinks that
   a. Einstein was never in love.
   b. Einstein had no personal life.
   c. Einstein's personal life was important.

4. Does the reviewer think this is a good book? _____

   How do you know? List some key words here: _____

   _____

Part Three

Evaluating Thinking Skills

These tests follow the same format as the Thinking Skills exercises in the Student Book. Thinking Skills exercises help students concentrate and think in English, at the same time giving them practice in many aspects of the thinking processes that are activated while reading. These include making inferences, guessing the meaning of new vocabulary, noticing relationship patterns, and reading critically. The difficulty of the exercises in the Student Book increases gradually as the student progresses through them.

There are three levels of Thinking Skills tests, with three tests at each level. It is important to give the tests after students have completed the appropriate Thinking Skills exercises in the Student Book.

Level One Tests: Give after students have completed Exercises 1–8, pages 161–166, in their Student Book.

Level Two Tests: Give after students have completed Exercises 9–16, pages 166–171, in their Student Book.

Level Three Tests: Give after students have completed Exercises 17–25, pages 172–179, in their Student Book.

Students should not use dictionaries while completing these tests.

Thinking Skills *Level One*

Test 1

➤ *Take this test after completing Exercises 1–8 in the Student Book (pages 161–166). Choose the best ending for each paragraph.*

1. Doctors say that everyone should eat lots of fruit and vegetables. They should eat some kind of fruit or vegetable at least five times a day. These foods help people to

   a. get rich.
   b. stay healthy.
   c. cook better.
   d. get sick.

2. The United States grows a lot of corn. Most of this corn is not eaten by people. It is

   a. used for food for small children.
   b. sold to people in other countries.
   c. used to feed cows, pigs, or chickens.
   d. made into bread, cakes, and cookies.

3. Each person in the United States uses about 450 liters of water a day. That is much more than in most other countries, especially in Africa. In Mozambique, for example, people use

   a. only about 10 liters per day.
   b. more than 450 liters per day.
   c. water every day.
   d. as much water as they want.

4. Wild animals often remind us of the place they come from. For example, a kangaroo reminds us of Australia, the penguin reminds us of the South Pole, and the lion reminds us of

   a. Africa.
   b. the zebra.
   c. the zoo.
   d. Europe.

5. In many hot countries, people do not work straight through the day. They start early and work until lunchtime. After lunch they rest for a few hours. Then they work

   a. until breakfast.
   b. the whole day.
   c. until evening.
   d. all morning.

Thinking Skills *Level One*

Test 2

➤ *Take this test after completing Exercises 1–8 in the Student Book (pages 161–166). Choose the best ending for each paragraph.*

1. Computers can be useful in elementary school. However, they are not useful if the teacher does not know how to use them or

   a. how much they cost.   c. what to say to them.
   b. when to go home.   d. how to teach with them.

2. Some animals, such as small birds, eat all day long. Other animals, like snakes, eat much less often. Some large snakes, for example, eat

   a. many meals a day.   c. for many years.
   b. just one meal a year.   d. many other animals.

3. The time in Hong Kong is exactly twelve hours ahead of the time in New York. When it is 7:00 in the morning in Hong Kong, it is

   a. 7:00 in the evening in New York.   c. midnight in New York.
   b. 7:00 in the morning in New York.   d. noon in New York.

4. The clothes moth is a kind of insect that eats clothes. It prefers clothes made of wool. If these moths get into your closet, your woolen clothes will

   a. not fit anymore.   c. get bigger.
   b. change color.   d. get holes in them.

5. The teacher says that the school will pay for the school trip. The parents are very happy about this. It means they will

   a. have to pay for it.   c. not have to pay for it.
   b. have to pay for the books.   d. not send their children on a
                                        school trip.

Thinking Skills *Level One*

Test 3

➤ *Take this test after completing Exercises 1–8 in the Student Book (pages 161–166). Choose the best ending for each paragraph.*

1. People are afraid of grizzly bears because they think these bears eat people. In fact, grizzlies do not often kill large animals of any kind. They eat mostly

   a. plants, fish, and small animals.   c. sheep, cows, and horses.
   b. other bears.   d. big fish and big animals.

2. In cities, people usually get their water from a central water supply. In the country, it is not always possible to get water from a central water supply. People often have to

   a. get water from a central water supply.   c. live far from the city.
   b. find their own water supply.   d. live without water.

3. In 1914 the Panama Canal opened to ships. They did not have to go around South America any more. This made world shipping much faster. For example, the trip from London to Tokyo was now

   a. about the same distance.   c. 4,500 miles longer.
   b. very long and difficult.   d. 4,500 miles shorter.

4. Honduras is a very mountainous country. In fact, only 14 percent of the land is flat enough for farming. For this reason, farmland in Honduras is

   a. very expensive.   c. very beautiful.
   b. not very expensive.   d. very poor.

5. Does anyone in your family have heart trouble? If so, then you should learn about heart attacks. Doctors say that the first few minutes after an attack are very important. If you know what to do, you can

   a. learn more about heart attacks.   c. save a person's life.
   b. give a person a heart attack.   d. call the doctor.

Thinking Skills *Level Two*

Test 1

➤ *Take this test after completing Exercises 9–16 in the Student Book (pages 166–171). Choose the best ending for each paragraph.*

1. Doctor "Patch" Adams is both a doctor and a clown. He helps sick people, especially children, by making them laugh. In fact,

   a. sick people often laugh.

   b. laughing can be dangerous to your health.

   c. laughing can help a sick person get better.

   d. many people laugh when there is a doctor.

2. Jacob and Wilhelm Grimm wrote their famous book of children's stories in 1812 in Germany. Now, almost 200 years later, the stories are popular around the world. Printed in 160 languages, the stories

   a. no longer interest most children.

   b. are enjoyed by children and adults.

   c. are interesting only to German children.

   d. tell us about Germany today.

3. Taking pictures of wild animals is not easy. They often run away before you can get close. If you get too close, they may not like it. They may get angry and

   a. go away.
   b. attack.

   c. take a picture.
   d. lie down.

4. Did you know that there are "dentist" fish? These small fish go into the mouths of larger fish and

   a. clean their teeth.
   b. open their mouths.

   c. have their dinner.
   d. look for trouble.

5. Scientists are studying the Arctic Ocean very closely these days. They are testing the water temperature and the ice. Studies show that the water is getting warmer and the

   a. ice is getting thicker.
   b. ice is getting thinner.

   c. days are getting longer.
   d. temperature is getting colder.

Thinking Skills *Level Two*

Test 2

➤ *Take this test after completing Exercises 9–16 in the Student Book (pages 166–171). Choose the best ending for each paragraph.*

1. The famous poem, the *Iliad,* describes the Trojan War. In this war, the ancient Greeks fought against the Trojans for the city of Troy. The poem tells all about

   a. the terrible effects of war.
   b. some people living in Greece.
   c. city life in present-day Troy.
   d. the ancient Greek poets.

2. In a large area of the midwestern United States, the 1930s were a difficult time. There was no rain for many years. The earth became very dry and the farms failed. The area became known as the

   a. Farm Bowl.
   b. Rain Bowl.
   c. Super Bowl.
   d. Dust Bowl.

3. In 1980, there were about 15,000 people over the age of 100 in the United States. By 1995, the number was almost double, and in the year 2000, it doubled again. More and more people are

   a. living in the United States.
   b. living to a very old age.
   c. dying at a younger age.
   d. having birthdays.

4. Most kinds of wild animals do not like to live near people. Skunks and raccoons are different. They like to live in towns or cities. They have few enemies there, and they

   a. like to eat only certain kinds of food.
   b. can find food in garbage cans and gardens.
   c. do not need to find any food.
   d. never find much food in garbage cans or gardens.

5. Many mushrooms grow in the forest. Some are good to eat, but others can make you very sick. It is not a good idea to

   a. find mushrooms in the forest.
   b. eat mushrooms from the forest.
   c. go for walks in the forest.
   d. grow mushrooms in the garden.

Name _____   Date _____

Thinking Skills *Level Two*

Test 3

➤ **Take this test after completing Exercises 9–16 in the Student Book (pages 166–171). Choose the best ending for each paragraph.**

1. People who live to a very old age have one thing in common. They almost all live in the country. Also, they usually work outdoors. Doctors believe that regular outdoor work

   a. is good for the garden.   c. helps you live longer.
   b. makes your life shorter.   d. makes you hungry.

2. In 1918, World War I came to an end. In the same year many people got Spanish influenza. This was a terrible kind of flu. It killed thousands of people around the world. In fact, many soldiers lived through the war, but later they

   a. went to Spain.   c. traveled around the world.
   b. died fighting.   d. died of flu.

3. The stork (a large bird) usually makes its home on the rooftops of houses. People believe that storks are good luck. They are happy when a stork

   a. makes its home in a tree.   c. flies over their house.
   b. lives on their house.   d. lives on someone else's house.

4. It is important to take good care of the roof of your house. A bad roof can cause many problems. If there are holes, the rain can go in. Then the walls and furniture may get

   a. dry.   c. wet.
   b. warm.   d. a new roof.

5. When people think of London they often think of rain. In fact, it gets fewer inches of rain every year than Tokyo or New York. People remember the rain in London because it

   a. almost never rains.   c. rains very often.
   b. is an old city.   d. is often very foggy.

Name _____ Date _____

Thinking Skills *Level Three*

Test 1

➤ *Take this test after completing Exercises 17–25 in the Student Book (pages 172–179). Choose the best ending for each paragraph.*

1. The frog is an animal that needs to live in or near water. These days, many small lakes and ponds are disappearing. People are filling them in to build houses and roads. This is one reason why there are fewer

   a. fish.
   b. animals.
   c. houses.
   d. frogs.

2. Recycled plastic bottles are usually made into new plastic bottles. They can also be made into many other things. They can even be made into material for clothes. This new material is used mostly for cold weather clothes, such as

   a. cotton and wool.
   b. sweaters and jackets.
   c. children and adults.
   d. T-shirts and shorts.

3. A desert is a place with less than 10 inches (254 millimeters) of rain in a year. We usually think of the desert as a very hot, dry place. In fact, it can also be a very cold, dry place. One example of this kind of desert is

   a. the Sahara.
   b. the sand.
   c. the Antarctic.
   d. Sweden.

4. The telephone was the invention of Alexander Graham Bell. We could say that it was his brainchild. First, he had an idea about a machine for talking over long distances. Then he worked on the idea until he had

   a. the first telephone.
   b. his first child.
   c. a large brain.
   d. another idea.

5. The grizzly bear is a very large animal that lives in Canada and the northern United States. Because grizzlies are so large, people are afraid of them. However, they are usually not dangerous. When a grizzly sees people it

   a. starts to run after them.
   b. runs around them in circles.
   c. usually runs away.
   d. often tries to kill them.

© 2001 by Addison Wesley Longman, Inc.
A Pearson Education company.
Duplication for classroom use is permitted.   **Reading Power Test Booklet**   *75*

Thinking Skills *Level Three*

Test 2

➤ *Take this test after completing Exercises 17–25 in the Student Book (pages 172–179). Choose the best ending for each paragraph.*

1. It is not difficult to make a kite. All you need is very light paper, thin wood sticks, and string. You do not need any special equipment. After all, the Chinese made kites 3,000 years ago and they didn't have

   a. power tools or plastics.
   b. paper or string.
   c. anything to make a kite with.
   d. kites.

2. The Jungfrau is a famous mountain in Switzerland. It was popular with mountain climbers in the nineteenth century and it is still very popular today. Only people with experience should try to climb it, however. It is not the highest mountain in Switzerland, but it is

   a. one of the least beautiful.
   b. not very interesting to climb.
   c. one of the most difficult to climb.
   d. one of many mountains in Switzerland.

3. If you are interested in dinosaurs, you should visit a dinosaur park. There are a number of them in the United States and in other countries. The dinosaurs in these parks are not real, of course. They are

   a. still only babies.
   b. life-size copies.
   c. dead.
   d. open to the public.

4. Elephants use their trunks in many ways. They use them to get leaves from trees and to get water to drink. They use them to make sounds and to "talk" to other elephants. They also use their trunks like a nose to

   a. feel and to touch.
   b. rest and to sleep.
   c. eat and to drink.
   d. breathe and to smell.

5. Many people think that chewing gum comes from the United States. In fact, people had chewing gum a very long time ago. Scientists recently found some 9,000-year-old chewing gum in Sweden. It still had

   a. footprints on it.
   b. fingerprints on it.
   c. teeth marks on it.
   d. tire prints on it.

Thinking Skills *Level Three*

Test 3

➤ *Take this test after completing Exercises 17–25 in the Student Book (pages 172–179). Choose the best ending for each paragraph.*

1. If a cat holds its tail up straight, that means it is happy. If the tail is moving from side to side, the cat is nervous. If the tail is not moving at all, the cat is probably asleep. You can learn a lot about a cat from

   a. its ears.   c. a book.
   b. its tail.   d. its owner.

2. Alexander the Great and Napoleon both were great men in their day. They also were both shorter than most other men. We can learn an important lesson from this: You can become great even if you are not

   a. rich.   c. tall.
   b. young.   d. short.

3. Madidi National Park in Bolivia covers 4.7 million acres. It is home to many kinds of birds—about 1,000 different species. This is many more than you can find anywhere in North America. In all of the United States and Canada, there are only 700 different

   a. acres of park land.   c. national parks.
   b. species of insects.   d. species of birds.

4. AIDS is a serious disease that kills millions of people every year. There are some new medicines that slow down or stop AIDS. However, these medicines are very expensive. In fact, most of the deaths from AIDS now are in

   a. poor countries.   c. North America.
   b. rich countries.   d. small countries.

5. The owl is a large bird that sleeps all day and stays awake at night. Some people are like these birds. They sleep late in the morning and stay awake late at night. In fact, they are sometimes called

   a. large birds.   c. day owls.
   b. night owls.   d. baby owls.

Part Four

Evaluating Reading Faster

─────

Some background information about Reading Faster

Before working on Part Four of the Student Book with students, it is important for teachers to have a good grasp of the rationale and objectives for the Reading Faster passages. This information can be found on pages 298–300 in the Teacher's Guide at the end of the Student Book.

It is essential that students also understand how their reading rate relates to comprehension and how regular practice with timed readings can help them learn to read faster. Thus, teachers should take special care in working through the Introduction to Part Four of the Student Book with students, taking the time to make sure that they understand fully the purpose of doing these exercises.

The effectiveness of the Reading Faster exercises depends on how the teacher approaches this work with the students. That is, students may tend to take this aspect of reading improvement less seriously than the comprehension skills exercises, or they may even refuse to accept the idea that learning to read faster is important. This attitude is partly because Part Four represents an approach to reading that may be novel to many students.

Why give grades on Reading Faster?

Students need to be evaluated on their work and progress with the timed readings. Teachers need to know how students are progressing so that they can encourage or correct where necessary. Furthermore, some form of testing inevitably gives reading-rate-improvement exercises more importance in the eyes of the students.

To evaluate students' work in Part Four: Reading Faster, teachers should look at each student's individual effort and progress. This evaluation, of course, may be complicated by the fact that reading rate depends on the content of the reading materials. A student who is familiar with New York, for example, might be able to read passage 25 very quickly. The same student, however, could find that his or her reading rate might slow down in passage 29 about Scotland. When this situation occurs, teachers will need to reassure students and explain to them how rate relates to content.

Guidelines for evaluating Reading Faster

Though the basis for evaluation must be tailored for each student, the method for evaluating need not be subjective. The following guidelines are intended to provide teachers with suggestions for establishing a systematic method for evaluating and grading students' improvement in reading rate.

1. If you plan to give students a grade for their progress in Reading Faster, ask them to tear out the Reading Faster Answer Key on page 287. Whenever students work on Reading Faster in class, you can hand out the Answer Keys for their use, collecting them afterward as you monitor students' work and their Progress Charts on pages 273 and 274.

2. Let the students know at the outset of the course that they will be evaluated on the basis of their individual progress, not in comparison to anyone else in the class or to some already established score or rate.

3. Tell the students that they will receive either S (satisfactory) or U (unsatisfactory) for grades on their Reading Faster work. To receive a grade of S, their reading rate will be evaluated on passages 19 and 20 and on passages 39 and 40. To receive a grade of S, students' average rate on those four passages, as compared with passages 1 and 2, should show an increase of 10 percent or more, with acceptable comprehension scores (at least 6 correct).

4. At the first class meeting, have the students tear out passages 19, 20, 39, and 40 in the Reading Faster section of their textbooks. The teacher should keep these passages and redistribute them when it is time to evaluate students' progress.

5. When the class has completed passage 18, hand out passages 19 and 20 for evaluation. The class is timed as usual, but without student access to the textbook. After they have finished reading and answering the questions on both passages, collect and score them. Record the scores in the Progress Chart on page 273. Follow the same procedure after the students have completed passage 38, and record the scores in the Progress Chart on page 274.

6. After correcting their answers and finding the students' reading rates, the teacher can compare students' work on the last two passages with their reading rate and comprehension scores on the first two passages, as recorded in their Progress Charts.

7. Students who make an effort will usually show more than a 10 percent improvement in their reading rates. It is not uncommon for a student to double his or her reading rate in one semester.

Answer Key

Note: For purposes of scoring, each item equals 1 point.

Unit 1: Scanning

Test 1, page 7
1. Five
2. South Pacific Cruise Lines and Olympia Cruises
3. Delta Princess Steamship
4. Famous Cruises and Royal Queen Cruises
5. Amsterdam Lines
6. 1-800-OLYMPICO
7. South Pacific, Antarctica
8. Three
9. P.O. Box 1234, Rosebud, NJ 98765-4321
10. April 1, 2003

Unit 2: Previewing and Predicting

Test 1, page 9
1. c
2. b
3. b
4. c
5. b
6. c
7. a
8. a

Test 2, page 11
1. b
2. c
3. c
4. a

Unit 3: Building a Powerful Vocabulary

Using the context to guess words

Test 1, page 13
1. home
2. wanted
3. pilot's
4. for
5. make
6. to
7. them
8. the
9. dangerous
10. did
11. flight
12. years
13. first
14. try
15. around
16. her
17. month
18. waiting
19. never
20. find

Test 2, page 15
1. seven
2. little
3. to
4. school
5. read
6. moved
7. then
8. job
9. down
10. him
11. time
12. decided
13. do
14. was
15. talk
16. books
17. all
18. Abraham
19. stop
20. while

Guessing meaning from context

In these tests, the answers may vary. The important thing is that students have good reasons for their answers.

Test 1, page 17
1. a grain made into a fine powder
2. when something disappears in a liquid
3. causing trouble or confusion
4. an area of land unchanged by humans
5. to begin a trip or journey

Test 2, page 18
1. the part of a shirt that covers the arms
2. strange and scary
3. make into small pieces or powder
4. dull, not sharp
5. hurt somebody or something with a sharp thing

Test 3, page 19
A.
1. g
2. l
3. a
4. f
5. c
6. i
7. j
8. k
9. e
10. b
11. h
12. d

B.
1. b
2. a
3. c
4. c
5. b

Test 4, page 21

A.

1.	h	7.	c
2.	b	8.	k
3.	j	9.	f
4.	a	10.	e
5.	d	11.	l
6.	i	12.	g

B.

1.	b	4.	a
2.	a	5.	b
3.	c		

Using pronouns

Test 1, page 23

2.	He	Eldridge Roberts
3.	it	his car
4.	He	Eldridge Roberts
5.	He	Eldridge Roberts
6.	He	Mr. Roberts
7.	he	Mr. Roberts
8.	He	the bus driver
9.	He	the bus driver
10.	It	the bus
11.	He	Mr. Roberts
12.	him	the driver
13.	It	the bus
14.	They	the passengers
15.	It	the bus
16.	it	the bus
17.	He	Mr. Roberts
18.	them	Mr. Roberts and the other passengers
19.	he	Mr. Roberts
20.	him	Mr. Roberts

Test 2, page 25

1.	they	Washington, D.C. and Washington State
2.	It	Washington State
3.	That	the biggest city
4.	it	a volcano named Mount St. Helens
5.	that	the Boeing factory
	it	the building
6.	them	parks
	it	Kobe Park
7.	them	immigrants
8.	them	very old, large trees
	that	people could cut them down
9.	them	islands
	they	people
10.	That	you can easily get to the mountains or the seaside

Test 3, page 26

1.	they	these people
	they	these people/Native Americans
2.	them	Native Americans
3.	they	Navajos
	It	a special house
4.	They	the Hopi Indians
	These	tall mountains with flat tops
5.	it	Phoenix
	this	growing very fast
6.	They	tourists
7.	it	Southwestern cooking
8.	It	Tucson
	it	Tuscon
9.	It	Flagstaff
10.	It	the Grand Canyon
	They	people
	it	the Grand Canyon

Using synonyms

Test 1, page 27

1. This part of the country
2. These vegetables
3. A lovely tune, such beautiful sounds
4. a place to live, home
5. an Italian city
6. the Internet, ways to communicate
7. these instruments, school orchestra
8. northwestern city, downtown area
9. This city, a place
10. colorful flowers, beautiful garden

Unit 4: Learning to Look for the Topic

Test 1, page 28

1. machines that help with housework (household appliances)
2. people who work in a restaurant
3. animals that live in the sea
4. kinds of food you need to make a cake
5. countries in southeast Asia
6. kinds of cars
7. instruments with strings
8. green vegetables
9. things you need for camping
10. hair colors

Test 2, page 29

1. places in Florida
2. things in a restaurant
3. kinds of material that are not natural
4. punctuation marks
5. kinds of flowers

6. things at a birthday party
7. ways for people to travel
8. electronic things in the home
9. world problems
10. sports you can do alone

Test 3, page 30
1. cities in Asia
2. sports played with a ball
3. parts of a rock band
4. kinds of fruit
5. geometric shapes
6. kinds of books
7. what happens when you have a cold (symptoms)
8. school subjects
9. kinds of housework
10. instruments you blow into (wind instruments)

Unit 5: Understanding Paragraphs
Any similar answers are acceptable.

Topics

Test 1, page 31
1.		2.		3.	
a.	too specific	a.	topic	a.	too general
b.	too general	b.	too specific	b.	too specific
c.	topic	c.	too general	c.	topic

Test 2, page 32
1.		2.		3.	
a.	topic	a.	too specific	a.	too general
b.	too specific	b.	too general	b.	topic
c.	too general	c.	topic	c.	too specific

Test 3, page 34
1. Topic: the job of firefighter
2. Topic: fighting forest fires
3. Topic: some rules to prevent fires

Test 4, page 35
1. Topic: farming today and farming 100 years ago in the United States
2. Topic: the special life of a farmer
3. Topic: farm work in the different seasons

Main ideas

Test 1, page 36
1. c   2. a   3. c

Test 2, page 38
1. a   2. c   3. b

Test 3, page 40
1. Main idea: Some plants from Madagascar are good medicines.
2. Main idea: In Madagascar people with health problems go to a healer.
3. Main idea: The plant medicines of Madagascar may help people around the world.

Test 4, page 41
1. Main idea: People in the United States use a lot of water.
2. Main idea: Many African countries do not have enough water.
3. Main idea: Countries with a lot of water may become rich.

Unit 6: Finding the Pattern of Organization
Any similar answers are acceptable.

Listing pattern

Test 1, page 42

1. Topic: the sports utility vehicle
Main idea: The sports utility vehicle is popular for several reasons.

Signal words:	Details:
First of all	it is larger
Also	it has four doors and a big back door
In addition	it is taller
Finally	it has more power
Also	it can go on rough roads

2. Topic: the SUV
Main idea: Some people do not like SUVs for a number of reasons.

Signal Words:	Details:
First	they are larger
Also	they are very heavy
Another	they are very expensive

3. Topic: SUVs
Main idea: There are two ways to solve the problems caused by SUVs.

Signal Words:	Details:
One way	change the way we think about them
Another way	change the cars

Time order pattern

Test 1, page 44

1. Topic: The early years of Venus and Serena Williams
Main idea: Venus and Serena Williams began playing tennis and competing when they were very young.

Signal Words:	Details:
1980, 1982	they were born
When they were still very young	they began to play in tournaments
1991	they stopped playing in junior tournaments
1991	they went to Florida

2. Topic: Venus and Serena Williams as teenagers
Main idea: They became famous and won many important tournaments when they were teenagers.

Signal Words:	Details:
1991 3	The Williams family moved to Florida.
1995	Venus and Serena became professional players.
By 1998	They were among the top ten players in the world.
1999	They played each other in an Australian tournament.

3. Topic: Venus and Serena in 1999, 2000
Main idea: In the years 1999 and 2000 Venus and Serena won the most famous tournaments and broke some records.

Signal Words:	Details:
Sept. 11, 1999	Serena won the U.S. Open.
The next day	Serena and Venus won the doubles tournament.
In July, 2000	Venus won at Wimbledon. They also won the doubles tournament.

Cause-and-effect pattern

Test 1, page 46

1. Topic: Plants and animals in the desert
Main idea: Because of the heat and dry weather, only some special plants and animals can live in the desert.

Causes:	Effects:
Desert heat and dry weather	Animals sleep during day, go out at night
	Animals sleep for months but wake up when it rains
	Seeds wait for rain, grow quickly, then plants live for only a few days

2. Topic: Irrigation in the desert
Main idea: The irrigation of desert land can cause some serious problems.

Cause:	Effects:
Irrigation of desert land	Underground water is used up
	Desert becomes drier
	Soil changes
	Plants will not grow in the soil

3. Topic: Larger deserts
Main idea: Many of the world's deserts are growing larger.

Causes:	Effects:
More people live near deserts	Deserts grow larger
Weather is hotter and drier	It is harder for plants to grow again

Comparison pattern

Test 1, page 48

1. The reasons why people left England for Australia and for the United States
Main idea: From the 1600s to the 1800s, people left England for Australia and North America for different reasons.

Likeness:	Differences:
Many people left England on ships for both Australia and North America.	People wanted to go to North America. They wanted a new life.
	People did not want to go to Australia. They were sent there as criminals.

2. The people in Australia and the U.S.
Main idea: The people in Australia and in the U.S. are similar in some ways.
Likeness:
There were native people before the English arrived.
The English fought and killed many native people.
The English took away the land and power of native people.
The native people could not vote until the 1960s.

3. Australia and the U.S. today
Main idea: Australia and the U.S. are different in most ways.

Likeness:	Differences:
They are almost the same size.	The population of the U.S. is much bigger.
	The governments are different.
	The geography is different.

Using all four patterns

Test 1, page 50
1. Sentence b   Pattern TO
2. Sentence a   Pattern L
3. Sentence e   Pattern C
4. Sentence c   Pattern CE

Test 2, page 52
1. Sentence c   Pattern TO
2. Sentence a   Pattern CE
3. Sentence e   Pattern L
4. Sentence b   Pattern C

Unit 7: **Making Inferences**
Any similar answers are acceptable.

Inferences from conversations

Test 1, page 54
A. 1. A new pet (probably a dog or a cat), which is causing some problems
   2. Can't tell
B. 1. What to cook for dinner with their friend, John
   2. In their home

Test 2, page 55
A. 1. A new student from Italy
   2. At college, maybe at a party
B. 1. An apartment for rent
   2. At the apartment

Inferences from stories

Test 1, page 56
1. A man named Marlowe
2. Detective
3. Derace Kingsley, his wife Crystal, a man named Lavery, a woman in a blue hat
4. Crystal was going out with Lavery. Lavery also went out with other women. Lavery was murdered. Marlowe found a gun on the floor of his room and Crystal's dress in his cupboard.
5. Marlowe will find out who the murderer is.

Test 2, page 57
1. Spillet, Pencroft, Herbert
2. On land near the sea, probably an island (because of the title of the book)

3. We don't know, but possibly because their ship went down.
4. They are trying to find all the necessary things for living there: food, water, a house.
5. They will make a life for themselves there and have some adventures.

Unit 8: **Skimming**

Skimming for point of view

Test 1, page 58
1. For
2. Against
3. For
4. Against
5. For
6. For
7. Against
8. For

Skimming for pattern of organization

Test 1, page 60
1. Comparison
2. Listing
3. Cause/effect
4. Time order
5. Comparison
6. Cause/effect
7. Comparison
8. Listing

Test 2, page 62
1. Cause/effect
2. Listing
3. Time order
4. Listing
5. Cause/effect
6. Time order
7. Listing
8. Comparison

Skimming for ideas

Test 1, page 64
1. b
2. c
3. b
4. Yes, a good story, better than the others, interesting, tells their story well, good history book, easy to read, important information

Test 2, page 66
1. c
2. a
3. c
4. Yes
enjoy this book

Evaluating Thinking Skills

Level One

Test 1, page 69
1. b
2. c
3. a

4. a
5. c

Test 2, page 70
1. d
2. b
3. a

4. d
5. c

Test 3, page 71
1. a
2. b
3. d

4. a
5. c

Level Two

Test 1, page 72
1. c
2. b
3. b

4. a
5. b

Test 2, page 73
1. a
2. d
3. b

4. b
5. b

Test 3, page 74
1. c
2. d
3. b

4. c
5. c

Level Three

Test 1, page 75
1. d
2. b
3. c

4. a
5. c

Test 2, page 76
1. a
2. c
3. b

4. d
5. c

Test 3, page 77
1. b
2. c
3. d

4. a
5. b